HUMAN DESIGN EVOLUTION GUIDE

Using the Solar Transits to Create Your Year

KAREN PARKER

2020 HUMAN DESIGN EVOLUTION GUIDE
Using the Solar Transits to Create Your Year
KAREN PARKER

Please visit QuantumAlignmentSystem.com
for more details, practitioners, and valuable resources.

@HumanDesignForEveryone   www.quantumalignmentsystem.com   @humandesignkaren

Published by GracePoint Matrix, LLC
Publishing Division
GracePointMatrix.com
ISBN: 978-1-951694-00-5

DEDICATION

To all my students, Human Design Specialists and Quantum Alignment Practitioners. Thank you for trusting me to be your teacher. Thank you for sharing the gift of Who You Truly Are with the world. I am because you are. I love you!

TABLE OF CONTENTS

INTRODUCTION

This book is a weekly guide designed to give you a deliberate way to harness the energy of the Sun and the Moon to support you in creating what you want in your life.

Human Design is a collection of cross-cultural, ancient and modern archetypes. An archetype is a pattern of thought or symbolic image that is derived from the past collective experience of humanity.

We experience all of the archetypes in the human design charts, either from our own unique charts, our relationships or through the planetary transits.

The colored in or "defined" elements in your Human Design chart tell you which archetypes you carry in your own chart. The "defined" elements in your chart are part of what you must master to bring your gifts into the world.

The white or "undefined" elements in your Human Design chart tell you a lot about what you are here to learn from others and from the world. You will experience these archetypes in a variety of different ways depending on who you are with and what energies are transiting in the celestial weather.

Over the course of a calendar year, the Sun moves through all 64 of the Human Design Gates. The Human Design Gates contain the energy code for 64 core human archetypes. As the sun moves through an archetype, it "lights up" that theme for everyone on the planet, creating a theme for the week.

We all deal with the weekly themes. Even if the theme doesn't impact your chart deeply, it will impact the charts of the people around you. The gift of the solar transits is that it gives you an opportunity to work deliberately with all 64 of these core human archetypes and to consciously focus on living the highest expression of these energies in your daily life. The solar transits also bring you creative energies that help you meet the goals you set for yourself each year.

The moon in Human Design represents the energy of what drives us. In traditional astrology, the new moon phase and the full moon phase represent bookend energies that mark the beginning and the end of a monthly creative cycle.

The new moon helps us set the intention for our goals for the month. The full moon supports us in releasing any energies, beliefs or blocks that are hindering the completion of our goals.

Lunar and solar eclipses are bookends that mark beginnings and endings. The work we do in between can be powerful, internal, as well as external. Eclipse energy represents cycles that support you in aligning more deeply with your bigger goals in life, as well as support you in breaking free from habits and patterns that keep you from growing and expanding.

To learn more about the transits and how they affect your personal Human Design chart and your energy click here: www.quantumalignmentsystem.com/solar-transit-calendar

HOW TO USE THIS BOOK

The 2020 Human Design Evolution Guide is a workbook with a weekly writing assignment, affirmations and Emotional Freedom Techniques (EFT) setup phrases. If you are not a fan of journaling, feel free to contemplate the prompts in whatever way works for you. You may walk with them, meditate on them or even discuss them with your friends.

This year I am excited to share with you updated Quantum Human Design language. Over the years it has become obvious to me the vocabulary in Human Design is in need of an upgrade in response to evolutionary shifts and with respect to new research that shows how the language we use is so powerful, it can even change your DNA. I hope you enjoy the new language!

Each of the Human Design Gates has a "challenge" associated with it. This is what you must master to get the most out of the movement of the Sun which occurs approximately every six days. Before you complete the writing assignment, read the "challenge" for each Gate and contemplate what you need to do to get the most out of each of the weekly archetypes.

The Emotional Freedom Techniques is a powerful energy psychology tool that has been scientifically proven to change your emotional, mental and genetic programming to help you express your highest potential. Each week you may work with a specific EFT setup phrase to help you clear any old energies you may be carrying related to the archetype of the week. (Learn more about how to use EFT here: www.quantumalignmentsystem.com/solar-transit-calendar)

You will also find exercises for each new moon, full moon, solar eclipse and lunar eclipse complete with a writing/contemplation assignment and affirmation. You'll be guided in working with the theme of the lunar cycles and eclipses so that you can make the most of these powerful energy cycles.

Every Human Design year gives us a 365 day creative cycle that supports us in releasing what no longer serves us, allows us to consciously increase our creative energy, grow, and evolve with the support of the stars.

May you have a prosperous and joyful 2020!

THE THEME OF THE YEAR

2020: The Year of Disruption

Each year contains powerful energy to support us on our personal and planetary evolutionary path. Every year carries a theme that is highlighted and repeats in multiple layers in the "celestial weather," including during moon cycles and eclipse cycles.

2020 promises to bring some big shakeups in the world. There are three big cycles that will impact us.

Jupiter and Pluto will be doing a celestial dance that promises to activate the potential for vast wealth, abundance, growth and expansion both personally and collectively. With this energy we will find ourselves redefining abundance and bringing our wealth into harmony with equitability and our faith. We will redefine what makes us wealthy and deepen our embrace of the energy of well-being as the currency of this new age.

Saturn and Pluto will bring us changes in the distrubution of power creating profound new understandings in the scientific fields of genetics, physics and quantum mechanics. This particular aspect has astrologers a little freaked out but I believe that as long as we are prepared and we remember Who We Truly Are, this shakeup promises to bring things back into alignment with integrity.

Saturn and Jupiter change from Earth energy to Air energy which can mark a significant shift in consciousness. We will be moving away from fossil fuels and cultivating new technology that is sustainable and clean. We will change our relationship with material gain and begin to share the resources of the world in such a way that reflects the value of every human being, regardless of race, age, religion. Barriers between people and nations will break down and people will begin to see themselves as One and as integral parts of all of Creation.

You were made for this time. Every single breath you've taken has prepared you to honor the call of your soul and serve as a guide for others.

The work you do on a personal level is a microcosm of the macrocosm of collective change. You are being invited by the planets to explore your relationship with your abundance, faith and power. The planets want you to remember that you are powerful, abundant and valuable simply because you exist. Your role this year is to erase old programming that may have caused you to forget Who You Truly Are.

May this be a blessed and prosperous year for you and may you remember the Magnificence of your Authentic Self.

From my Heart to Yours,

Karen

JANUARY 10, 2020

PENUMBRAL LUNAR ECLIPSE

 19:11 GMT

 19 DEGREES 54 MINUTES CANCER

☾ MOON IN GATE 53

This year's Evolution Guide actually starts before the Human Design New Year begins (on January 23, 2020) with the Lunar Eclipse on January 10 in Gate 53, the Gate of Starting.

Eclipses act like "bookends" that set the tone for the work that we do in between each eclipse. This particular eclipse cycle ends on June 5, 2020 with the lunar eclipse in Gate 5, the Gate of Consistency.

The celestial weather in between these eclipses promises to bring us a beginning to our year that is full of disruption and shakeups. It's a year that requires of us the focus, to allow the outer circumstances to initiate our faith and our ability to stay aligned and create in the direction which we intend, no matter what our outer reality looks like. We are being taught to keep our "eye on the prize" no matter what and to remember that our ability to stay focused is the skill set we must cultivate in order to grow and evolve. If we fail to focus, we create by default and run the risk of being victimized by our own lack of focus.

This first Lunar Eclipse asks you to to respond in alignment with your energy blueprint to opportunities to get things started, to initiate the process of preparing or "setting the stage" for the manifestation of a dream before it becomes a reality, to learn to trust in the timing of the Universe and not take charge and try to implement your own will while working against Divine Timing.

We are encouraged to be in the flow of timing and not burn out trying to complete things that are not ours to complete or go against right timing. We are learning to find peace with starting and trusting the Universe to finish the plan in the appropriate way.

JOURNAL QUESTIONS:

Stay tuned this week to the energy of new beginnings and starting things. Allow the ideas, revelations, inspirations and spurts of initiation energy to rev up your engines but wait according to your strategy to jump in! Make a list of your new ideas or your renewed inspirations.

 AFFIRMATION:

I am a servant to Divine Inspiration. My thoughts, inspirations and ideas set the stage for creative expansion and the potential for evolution. I take action on the ideas that present themselves to me in an aligned way. I honor all other ideas knowing that my gift is in the spark of energy that gets things rolling when the timing is right. While I wait for right timing, I guard my energy and charge my battery so that I am sustainable when the time is right for action.

JANUARY 23, 2020

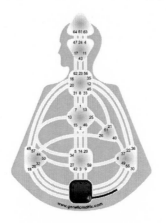

www.geneticmatrix.com

HEXAGRAM 41 - IMAGINATION

 CHALLENGE:

To learn to use your imagination as a source of creative inspiration and manifestation. To experience the world and imagine more abundant possibilities. To stay connected to your creative fire.

 JOURNAL QUESTIONS:

1. Do I own my creative power? How can I deepen my self-honoring of my creative power?

AFFIRMATION:

I am a creative nexus of inspiration for the world. My ideas and imaginings inspire people to think beyond their limitations. My ideas stimulate new possibilities in the world. I am a powerful creator; my creative thoughts, ideas and inspirations set the stage for miracles and possibilities that will change the story of humanity.

 ## EFT SETUP:

Even though I'm afraid my dreams won't come true, I deeply and completely love and accept myself.

JANUARY 24, 2020

NEW MOON

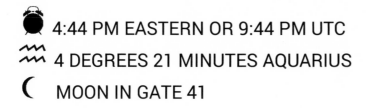

🕮 4:44 PM EASTERN OR 9:44 PM UTC

♒ 4 DEGREES 21 MINUTES AQUARIUS

☾ MOON IN GATE 41

New moon energy invites us to explore how we can deepen our alignment with our intentions and asks us to focus on what we want to grow and expand on in our lives.

The New Moon in Gate 41 brings us the energy of new beginnings. The Human Design year starts with this energy and adding the potential of imagination to the initiating power of the New Moon creating the capacity for us to experience an amplified new beginning to this powerful year.

New moon energy is always about starting a creative process. Gate 41, Imagination, invites us to take a look around at our life and to see what we want to expand on and what we want to let go of so that we have more.

This is an important time to take the time to imagine, envision, visualize and fantasize about what else is possible for your life. What do you have going on that you'd like more of?

You are mastering your ability to use your creative imagination to generate ideas about new abundant opportunities in the world, to sustain these abundant visions, share them when necessary and to use your imagination to break old patterns and limiting beliefs. This is your chance to be able to hold the vision of a miracle that transcends expectations.

JOURNAL QUESTIONS:

1. What do I need to do deepen my connection with Source? Do I feel aligned with something bigger than myself? Do I need to create a routine in my daily practice to stay centered and connected?

 AFFIRMATION:

In the stillness I surrender to the Great Mystery of Life and the Divine. I allow Divine Inspiration to wash over me and I listen with great attention and appreciation. I trust that I receive the perfect inspiration and I simply let the inspiration flow to me. I am grateful.

JANUARY 28, 2020

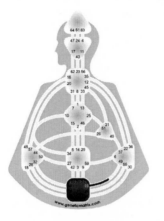

HEXAGRAM 19 - ATTUNEMENT

 CHALLENGE:

To learn how to manage being a highly sensitive person and not let your sensitivity cause you to compromise what you want and who you are. To learn to keep your own resources in a sustainable state in order so that you have more to give. To not martyr yourself to the needs of others. To learn how to become emotionally intimate without being shut down or co-dependent.

 JOURNAL QUESTIONS:

1. Am I emotionally present in my relationships? Do I need to become more attuned to my own emotional needs and ask for more of what I want and need?

AFFIRMATION:

I am deeply aware of the emotional needs and energy of others. My sensitivity and awareness gives me insights that allow me to create intimacy and vulnerability in my relationships. I am aware and attuned to the emotional frequency around me and I make adjustments to help support a high frequency of emotional alignment. I honor my own emotional needs as the foundation of what I share with others.

 ## EFT SETUP:

Even though it's scary to open my heart, I now choose to create space for deep intimacy and love in my life and I deeply and completely love and accept myself.

FEBRUARY 3, 2020

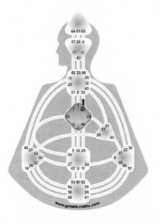

HEXAGRAM 13: NARRATIVE

 CHALLENGE:

To forgive the past and redefine who you are each and every day. To tell a personal narrative that is empowering, self-loving and reflects your value and your authentic self. To bear witness to the pain and narrative of others and offer them a better story that allows them to expand on their abundance and blessings.

 JOURNAL QUESTIONS:

1. *What stories about my life am I holding on to?*

2. *Do these stories reflect who I really am and what I want to create in my life?*

3. *What or who do I need to forgive in order to liberate myself to tell a new story?*

4. *What secrets or stories am I holding for others? Do I need to release them?*

5. *Write the true story of who I really am….*

 AFFIRMATION:

The story that I tell myseld and the one I tell the world, sets the tone and direction for my life.I am the artist and creator of my story. I have the power to rewrite my story every day. The true story I tell from my Heart allows me to serve my Right Place in the Cosmic Plan.

✋ **EFT SETUP:**

Even though I'm afraid to speak my truth, I now share the truth from my heart and trust that I am safe and I deeply and completely love and accept myself.

FEBRUARY 8, 2020

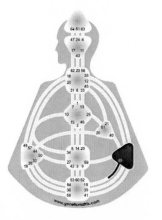

HEXAGRAM 49: REVOLUTION

 CHALLENGE:

To not quit prematurely, failing to start a necessary revolution in your life, to not hold on to unhealthy situations, relationships or agreements that may compromise your value and worth.

 JOURNAL QUESTIONS:

1. Am I holding on too long? Is there a circumstance and condition that I am allowing because I am afraid of the emotional energy associated with change?

2. Do I have a habit of quitting too soon? Do I fail to do the work associated with creating genuine intimacy?

3. What do I need to let go of right now to create room for me to align with higher principles?

 ## AFFIRMATION:

I am a cosmic revolutionary. I am aligned with higher principles that support the evolution of humanity. I stand for peace, equity and sustainability. I align with these principles and I stand my ground. I do the work to create the intimacy necessary to share my values with others. I value myself and my work enough to only align with relationships that support my vital role.

 ## EFT SETUP:

Even though my emotional response causes me to react/paralyze me, I deeply and completely love and accept myself.

FEBRUARY 9, 2020

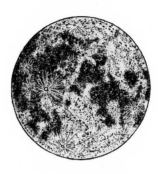

FULL MOON

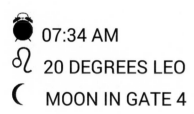

07:34 AM

20 DEGREES LEO

MOON IN GATE 4

Full moon energy invites us to explore what we need to release and let go of in order to stay in alignment with our intentions.

Gate 4, the Gate of Possibility, gives us a reminder that ideas are "seeds" and that our job is not to figure out how to manifest the idea but to nurture the "seed" of the idea with our imagination. We then, in turn, use the power of our imaginations to stimulate emotional energy which tunes our Heart energy and influences the opportunities we notice and attract into our lives.

This full moon invites you to release any self-doubt or fear you may have about your ideas, to simply serve as a "steward" for Divine Inspiration and to trust that the unfolding of your idea will happen naturally when you stay curious and open to possibility.

 JOURNAL QUESTIONS:

1. *What ideas do I have right now that need me to nurture and activate them?*

2. What possibilities do these ideas stimulate right now? Take some time to write or visualize these possibilities.

3. Am I comfortable with waiting? What can I do to increase my patience and curiosity?

 AFFIRMATION:

I am tuned into the cosmic flow of possibility. I am inspired about exploring new possibilities and potentials. I use the power of my thoughts to stretch the limits of what is known and engage my imagination to explore the potential of the unknown.

FEBRUARY 14, 2020

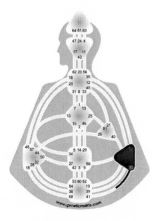

HEXAGRAM 30: PASSION

 CHALLENGE:

To be able to sustain a dream or a vision without burning out. To know which dream to be passionate about. To not let passion overwhelm you and to wait for the right timing to share your passion with the world.

 JOURNAL QUESTIONS:

1. *What am I passionate about? Have I lost my passion?*

2. *How is my energy? Am I physically burned out? Am I burned out on my idea?*

3. *What do I need to do to sustain my vision or dream about what I am inspired to create in my life?*

4. Do I have a dream or vision I am avoiding because I'm afraid it won't come true?

 ## AFFIRMATION:

I am a passionate creator. I use the intensity of my passion to increase my emotional energy and sustain the power of my dream and what I imagine for Life. I trust in the Divine flow and I wait for the right timing and the right circumstances to act on my dream.

 ## EFT SETUP:

Even though my excitement feels like fear, I now choose to go forward with my passion on fire, fully trusting the infinite abundance of the Universe and I deeply and completely love and accept myself.

FEBRUARY 19, 2020

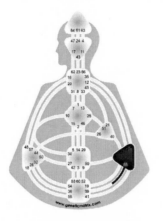

HEXAGRAM 55: FAITH

 CHALLENGE:

To learn to trust Source. To know that you are fully supported. To master the art of emotional alignment AS your most creative power.

 JOURNAL QUESTIONS:

1. *Do I trust that I am fully supported? What do I need to do to deepen that trust?*

2. *How can I align myself with abundant emotional energy? What practices or shifts do I need to make in my life to live and create in a more aligned way?*

3. *Do I surround myself with beauty? How can I deepen my experience of beauty in my life?*

4. What do I have faith in now? What old gods of limitation do I need to stop worshipping?

5. Go on a miracle hunt. Take stock of everything good that has happened in my life. How much "magic" have I been blessed with?

 AFFIRMATION:

I am perfectly and divinely supported. I know that all my needs and desires are being fulfilled. My trust in my support allows me to create beyond the limitation of what others think is possible and my faith shows them the way. I use my emotional energy as the source of my creative power. My frequency of faith lifts others up and opens up a greater world of potential and possibility.

 **EFT SETUP:**

Even though I struggle with faith and trusting Source, I deeply and completely love and accept myself.

FEBRUARY 23, 2020

NEW MOON

03:33 PM UTC

♓ 4 DEGREES 28 MINUTES PISCES

☾ MOON IN GATE 55

New moon energy invites us to explore how we can deepen our alignment with our intentions and asks us to focus on what we want to grow and expand on in our lives.

Gate 55 is the Gate of Faith. This new moon expansion is an invitation from the planets to deepen our trust in Source and our faith that the vision we hold, even when still unseen, is on its way into our life.

This energy, with proper emotional alignment and deep faith, gives us a foundation of creativity that ensures that all of our needs will be met and we will have everything we need to fulfill our **Life Purpose** when we trust **Source**.

This invites us to create without limitation, without compromise and in an unapologetically authentic way. With New Moon energy lighting this archetype up, we're being invited to explore what we *really* want and to tend to our dreams with great expectations of fulfillment.

JOURNAL QUESTIONS:

1. What do I need to do to release any worries and fears I may have about abundance in my life? What beliefs do I have about being fully supported and abundant? Do I need to align these beliefs with what I know is Truth?

2. What does being aware of the Abundance of Spirit within me feel like? What does it look like? How would being constantly aware of this fulfilling energy change my life? What do I need to do to be ready for this level of faith and trust?

 AFFIRMATION:

I am aware of the Abundance of Spirit within me. I know that when I am focused on this Abundance in Spirit that all my desires are fulfilled and it is impossible for me to experience lack or need. I am completely supported and fulfilled by this awareness. By letting go and letting God, I allow abundance in all aspects of my life to manifest fully for me. Abundance is my birthright and my natural state.

FEBRUARY 25, 2020

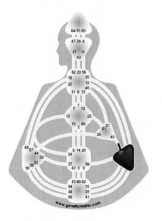

HEXAGRAM: 37 - HARMONY

 ## CHALLENGE:

To find inner peace as the true source to outer peace. To not let chaos and outer circumstances knock you off your center and disrupt your peace.

 ## JOURNAL QUESTIONS:

1. What habits, practices and routines do I have that cultivate my inner alignment with sustainable peace?

2. When I feel that my outer world is chaotic and disrupted how do I cultivate inner peace?

3. What do I need to do to cultivate a peaceful emotional frequency?

AFFIRMATION:

I am an agent of peace. My being, aligned with peace, creates an energy of contagious peace around me. I practice holding a peaceful frequency of energy and I respond to the world with an intention of creating sustainable peace.

 ## EFT SETUP:

Even though I struggle to create peace and harmony in my life, I deeply and completely love and accept myself.

MARCH 2, 2020

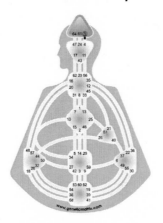

HEXAGRAM 63 - CURIOSITY

 CHALLENGE:

To not let self-doubt and suspicion cause you to stop being curious.

 JOURNAL QUESTIONS:

1. Am I curious about life? Do I regularly allow myself to be curious about what else is possible in the world? In my life?

2. Do I doubt myself and my ideas?

3. What needs to happen for me to unlock my need to be right about an idea and to allow myself to dream of possibilities again?

AFFIRMATION:

My curiosity makes me a conduit of possibility thinking. I ask questions that stimulate imaginations. I allow the questions of my mind to seed dreams that stimulate my imagination and the imagination of others. I share my questions as an opening to the fulfillment of potential in the world.

 ## EFT SETUP:

Even though I struggle with trusting myself, I now choose to relax and know that I know. I listen to my intuition. I abandon logic and let my Higher Knowing anchor my spirit in trust and I deeply and completely love and accept myself.

MARCH 7, 2020

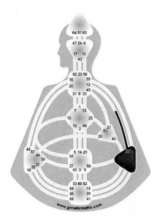

HEXAGRAM 22 - SURRENDER

 CHALLENGE:

To trust that your passions and deepest desires are supported by the Universal flow of abundance. To have the courage to follow your passion and know that you'll be supported. To learn to regulate your emotional energy so that you have faith that everything will unfold perfectly.

 JOURNAL QUESTIONS:

1.   Where am I denying my passion in my life? Where have I settled for less than what I want because I'm afraid I can't get what I want?

2.   What do I need to do to fully activate my passion? What is one bold step towards my genius that I could take right now?

3. Do I trust the Universe? What do I need to do to deepen my trust?

4. Do I have a regular practice that supports me in sustaining a high frequency of emotional energy and alignment?

5. What needs to be healed, released, aligned and brought to my awareness for me to deepen my faith?

 ## AFFIRMATION:

I am a global change agent. I am inspired with passions that serve the purpose of transforming the world. I trust that my emotions and my passion will align me with faith and the flow of resources I need to do to fulfill my life purpose. When I let go and follow my passion, I am given everything I need to change the world.

 ## EFT SETUP:

Even though it's hard to trust in my support, I now choose to trust anyway and I deeply and completely love and accept myself.

MARCH 9, 2020

FULL MOON

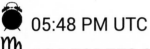 05:48 PM UTC

♍ 19 DEGREES 36 MINUTES VIRGO

☾ MOON IN GATE 47

Full moon energy invites us to explore what we need to release and let go of in order to stay in alignment with our intentions.

This Full Moon in Gate 47, the Gate of Mindset, encourages us to explore how our mindset and our expectations of fulfillment are influencing what we believe is possible for our lives right now.

This important Gate is part of the stream of expansion. When we are masterful of this energy, we serve as "stewards" for our ideas, trusting the instructions and the path for manifesting our ideas will be revealed to us when the time is right.

We are being invited to explore how much we are willing to expand our creative capacity. What do we need to release in order to allow for more in our lives. Do we have limitations and old beliefs that keep us from truly allowing our dreams to be fulfilled.

JOURNAL QUESTIONS:

1. What things will I do while I am waiting for my manifestation? What will I do to keep my vibration high while I wait? What is the status of my mindset? Do I need to take care of my thought patterns?

 AFFIRMATION:

I wait with delighted anticipation and marvel and the curious way the Universe manifests my desires. I keep my mindset joyful and positive and I only focus on the end result.

MARCH 13, 2020

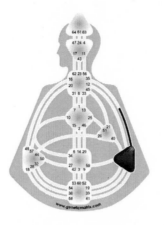

HEXAGRAM 36 - EXPLORATION

 CHALLENGE:

To not let boredom cause you to leap into chaos. To learn to stick with something long enough to become masterful and to bear the fruits of your experience.

 JOURNAL QUESTIONS:

1. How does boredom impact my life? What do I do when I feel bored? What can I do to keep myself aligned even when I'm bored?

2. What stories have I experienced that have shattered old patterns and expectations? How have my stories changed or inspired others?

3. What do I do to maintain or sustain emotional alignment? What do I need to add to my daily practice to "amp" up my emotional energy around my intentions?

_____

 AFFIRMATION:

My experiences and stories break old patterns and push the boundaries of the edge of what's possible for humanity. I defy the patterns and I create miracles through my emotional alignment with possibility. I hold my vision and maintain my emotional energy as I wait to bear the fruit of my intentions and my visions.

✋ **EFT SETUP:**

Even though it's scary to be out of my comfort zone, I now choose to push myself into something new and more aligned with my Truth and I deeply and completely love and accept myself.

MARCH 18, 2020

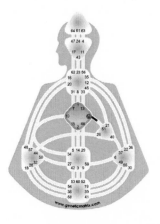

HEXAGRAM 25 - SPIRIT

 CHALLENGE:

To trust the Divine Order in all of your life. To learn to connect with Source as the path to creating well-being in your life. To remember that your life serves an irreplaceable role in the cosmic plan and to honor that role and to live from it. To trust Source.

 JOURNAL QUESTIONS:

1. *Do I trust Source?*

2. *Do I have a regular practice that connects me to Source?*

3. Do I know my Life Purpose? Am I living true to my Purpose? How can I deepen my connection to my Purpose?

 ## AFFIRMATION:

I am an agent of the Divine. My life is the fulfillment of Divine Order and the Cosmic Plan. When I am connected to Source, I serve my right place. I take up no more than my space and no less than my place in the world. I serve and through serving, I am supported.

✋ EFT SETUP:

Even though in the past, I was afraid to follow my heart, I now choose to do what is right for me and know that I am fully supported and I deeply and completely love and accept myself.

MARCH 24, 2020

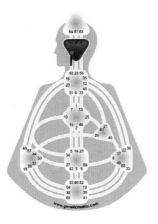

HEXAGRAM 17 - ANTICIPATION

 CHALLENGE:

To learn to share your thoughts about possibilities only when people ask for them. To not let doubt and suspicion keep you from seeing the potential of positive outcomes.

 JOURNAL QUESTIONS:

1.   What do I need to do to manage my insights and ideas so that they increase the options and potential of others?

2. How do I feel about holding back from sharing my insights until the timing is right? What can I do to manage my need to share without waiting for the right timing?

3. What routines and strategies do I need to cultivate to keep my perspectives expanding and possibility oriented?

4. How can I improve my ability to manage doubt and fear?

 ## AFFIRMATION:

I use the power of my mind to explore possibilities and potential. I know that the inspirations and insights that I have create exploration and experimentation that can inspire the elegant solutions necessary to master the challenges facing humanity.

 ## EFT SETUP:

Even though I have a lot of ideas and thoughts to share, I trust that the insights that I have to offer are too important to blurt out and I wait for the right people to ask and I deeply and completely love and accept myself.

MARCH 24, 2020

NEW MOON

 09:29 AM UTC

♈ 4 DEGREES 12 MINUTES ARIES

☾ MOON IN GATE 17

New moon energy invites us to explore how we can deepen our alignment with our intentions and asks us to focus on what we want to grow and expand on in our lives.

The New Moon in Gate 17, the Gate of Anticipation, encourages us to continue to expand on what we think is possible for our lives. We are being invited to anticipate and prepare for the manifestation of our next creation.

You are learning to use the power of your mind to explore potentials and possibilities that stretch your ideas about what else is possible in your life and in the human condition.

You are being invited to explore how to use your thoughts to inspire others to think bigger and bolder and to use your words to inspire and set the stage for creating energy that expands your potential and the potential of the world.

JOURNAL QUESTIONS:

1. What do I do with ideas and inspirations that spark my enthusiasm? Am I good at holding on to ideas and allowing the right people to be drawn to the "germinating" phase of my creation?

2. What does the phrase "to serve" mean to me? Am I being of service? Do I need to do more service? Am I serving myself as the foundation of the service I offer? Can I serve myself without guilt?

 AFFIRMATION:

I use the power of my mind to explore possibilities and potential. I know that the inspirations and insights that I have create exploration and experimentation that can inspire the elegant solutions necessary to master the challenges facing humanity.

MARCH 30, 2020

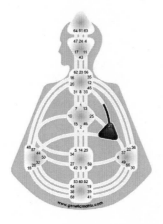

HEXAGRAM 21 - SELF-REGULATION

 CHALLENGE:

To learn to let go. To master self-regulation. To release the need to control others and circumstances. To trust in the Divine and to know that you are supported. Knowing that you are worthy of support and you don't have to over-compensate.

 JOURNAL QUESTIONS:

1. *Where do I need to release control in my life?*

2. *Do I trust the Universe?*

3. *Do I value myself? Do I trust that I'll be supported in accordance with my value?*

4.   What do I need to do to create an internal and external environment of self-generosity?

5.   What needs to be healed, released, aligned and brought to my awareness for me to embrace my true value?

 AFFIRMATION:

I am worthy of claiming, protecting and defending my rightful place in the world. I create an inner and outer environment that is self-generous and I regulate my environment to sustain a high frequency of alignment with my true value. I know that I am an irreplaceable and precious part of the cosmic plan and I create my life to reflect the importance of my right place in the world.

 EFT SETUP:

Even though in the past I felt like I had to control everything, I now surrender to Source and know that my abundance, my TRUE abundance, is available to me when I let go and let the Universe do the work and I deeply and completely love and accept myself.

APRIL 4, 2020

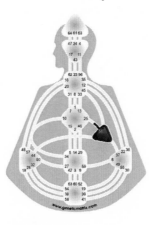

HEXAGRAM 51 - INITIATION

 **CHALLENGE:**

To not let the unexpected cause you to lose your faith. To not let a pattern of unexpected events cause you to lose your connection with your purpose and Source. To learn to use the power of your own story of initiation to initiate others into fulfilling their rightful place in the Cosmic Plan.

 JOURNAL QUESTIONS:

1. *What has shock and the unexpected taught me in my life?*

2. *How can I deepen my connection to Source?*

3. *How can my experiences of initiation be shared with others? What am I here to "wake people up" to?*

 ## AFFIRMATION:

I navigate change and transformation with Grace. I know that when my life takes a twist or a turn, it is my soul calling me out to serve at a higher level. I use disruption as a catalyst for my own growth and expansion. I am a teacher and an initiator. I use my ability to transform pain into growth and power to help others navigate through crisis and emerge on the other side of crisis empowered and aligned.

 ## EFT SETUP:

Even though things aren't turning out like I expected, I now choose to embrace the unexpected and trust that the Universe is always serving my Greater Good and I deeply and completely love and accept myself.

APRIL 8, 2020

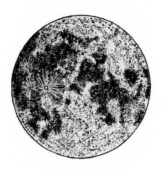

FULL MOON

 02:35 AM UTC

 18 DEGREES 42 MINUTES LIBRA

☾ MOON IN GATE 57

Full moon energy invites us to explore what we need to release and let go of in order to stay in alignment with our intentions.

The Full Moon in Gate 57, the Gate of Instinct, invites us to release anything that is keeping us from trusting ourselves and our own personal connection to our intuition and to Source.

Gate 57 has a still, inner voice that gives a pulse to let you know when the timing is right to take action. It asks you to prepare for the future, to get ready for what's next. The challenge is that we often discount that voice because the messages it sends us often defy our rational and logical knowledge. We don't know how we know so we mistrust our knowing.

This Full Moon is asking us to deepen our self-trust, to grow in our connection with our own intuition and to listen to our own inner wisdom, even if it defies what our minds think is possible.

JOURNAL QUESTIONS:

1. Do I trust my intuition? What does my intuition feel like to me?

2. Sometimes doing a retrospective analysis of my intuition/instinct makes it more clear how my intuitive signal works. What experiences in the past have I had that I "knew" I should or shouldn't do? How have I experienced my intuition in the past?

3. When I think about moving forward in my life, do I feel afraid? What am I afraid of? What can I do to mitigate the fear?

4. What impulses am I experiencing that are telling me to prepare for what's next in my life? Am I acting on my impulses? Why or why not?

 AFFIRMATION:

My Inner Wisdom is deeply connected to the pulse of Divine Timing. I listen to my Inner Wisdom and follow my instinct. I know when and how to prepare the way to prepare for the future. I take guided action and I trust myself and Source.

APRIL 10, 2020

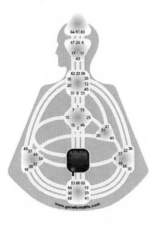

HEXAGRAM 42 - CONCLUSION

 CHALLENGE:

To learn to bring things to completion. To allow yourself to be led to where you need to be to finish things. To value your ability to know how to finish and to learn to give up your need to try to start everything. To finish things in order to create space for something new.

JOURNAL QUESTIONS:

1. *Do I own and value my natural gift of knowing how to bring things to completion?*

2. *What things in my life do I need to finish in order to make room for something new?*

3. Am I holding on to old circumstances and patterns because I'm afraid to let them go?

4. Do I judge myself for "not starting things"? How can I learn to be gentler with myself?

AFFIRMATION:

I am gifted at knowing when and how to finish things. I respond to bringing events, experiences and relationships to a conclusion in order to create space for something new and more abundant. I can untangle the cosmic entanglements that keep people stuck in old patterns. My ability to re-align and complete things helps others create space for transformation and expansion.

EFT SETUP:

Even though I've hesitated in the past to finish what I needed to finish in order to make room for something new and better, I now choose to bring things to a powerful ending. I know that I am taking strong action to create space for what I truly want to create in my life and I deeply and completely love myself.

APRIL 16, 2020

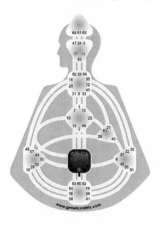

HEXAGRAM 3 - INNOVATION

 CHALLENGE:

To learn to trust in Divine Timing and to know that your ideas and insights will be transmitted to the world when the world is ready.

 JOURNAL QUESTIONS:

1. *Where has Divine Timing worked out in my life? What has waiting taught me?*

2. *Do I trust in Divine Timing?*

3. *If the opportunity to share my ideas with the world presented itself today, would I be ready? If not, what do I need to prepare to be ready?*

AFFIRMATION:

I am here to bring change to the world. My natural ability to see what else is possible to create something new is my strength and my gift. I patiently cultivate my inspiration and use my understanding of what is needed to help evolve the world.

 ## EFT SETUP:

Even though it's scary to take the first step, I now trust the Universe and my ability to be innovative and know that I stand on the cusp of the fulfillment of my Big Dreams. I deeply and completely love and accept myself.

APRIL 22, 2019

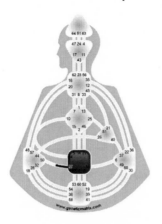

HEXAGRAM 27 - ACCOUNTABILITY

 CHALLENGE:

To care without over-caring. To allow others to assume responsibility for their own challenges and choices. To learn to accept other people's values. To not let guilt cause you to compromise what is good and right for you.

 JOURNAL QUESTIONS:

1. Am I taking responsibility for things that aren't mine to be responsible for? Whose problem is it? Can I return the responsibility for the problem back to its rightful owner?

2. What role does guilt play in motivating me? Can I let go of the guilt? What different choices might I make if I didn't feel guilty?

3. What obligations do I need to set down in order for me to take better care of myself?

4. Are there places where I need to soften my judgements of other people's values.

 ## AFFIRMATION:

I have a nurturing and loving nature. It is my gift to be able to love and care for others. I know that the greatest expression of my love is to treat others as capable and powerful. I support when necessary and I let go with love so my loved ones can discover their own strength and power.

 ## EFT SETUP:

Even though it's hard to say no, I now choose to take the actions that are correct for me. I release my guilt and I deeply and completely love and accept myself.

APRIL 23, 2020

NEW MOON

 02:27 AM UTC

♉ 3 DEGREES 23 MINUTES TAURUS

☾ MOON IN GATE 27

New moon energy invites us to explore how we can deepen our alignment with our intentions and asks us to focus on what we want to grow and expand on in our lives.

This new moon in Gate 27, the Gate of Accountability, is inviting us to explore our relationship agreements and dynamics. This energy brings a tremendous amount of potential for nurturing and caring. This can sometimes lead to over-caring or co-dependent relationship patterns that can be depleting and devaluing.

When we are exploring this energy with the New Moon, we are being asked to evaluate our relationship patterns, to discover if our relationships are sustainable and aligned with values that empower and encourage evolution and growth. This is a good week to ask yourself if you are regularly doing things for others that they could be doing for themselves and to invite those you love to assume responsibility for their own challenges as part of their own evolutionary path.

We're also reminded that we can't take care of others if our own resources are depleted. You cannot give from an empty cup. Do you need to sustain yourself in better, more restorative ways so that you have more to give in your relationships?

JOURNAL QUESTIONS:

1.   Am I taking responsibility for things that aren't mine to be responsible for? Whose problem is it? Can I return the responsibility for the problem back to its rightful owner?

2.   What role does guilt play in motivating me? Can I let go of the guilt? What different choices might I make if I didn't feel guilty?

3. What obligations do I need to set down in order for me to take better care of myself?

4. Are there places where I need to soften my judgements on other people's values.

 ## AFFIRMATION:

I have a nurturing and loving nature. It is my gift to be able to love and care for others. I know that the greatest expression of my love is to treat others as capable and powerful. I support when necessary and I let go with love so that my loved ones can discover their own strength and power.

APRIL 27, 2020

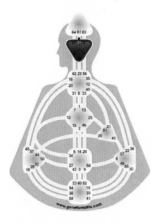

HEXAGRAM 24 - BLESSINGS

 CHALLENGE:

To learn to allow what you truly deserve in your life. To not rationalize an experience that allowed for thess than you deserve. To find the blessings and power from painful experiences and to use them as catalysts for transformation.

 JOURNAL QUESTIONS:

1. What are the blessings I learned from my greatest painful experiences? Can I see how these experiences served to teach me? What did I learn?

2. What am I grateful for from the past?

3. Where might I be rationalizing staying stuck or settling for less than what I really want or deserve? What do I need to do to break out of this pattern?

AFFIRMATION:

I embrace the Mystery of Life with the awareness that the infinite generosity of the Universe gives me blessings in every event in my life. I find the blessings from the pain. I grow and expand beyond the limitations of my experiences and stories. I use what I have learned to create a life and circumstances that reflect the miracle that I am.

✋ EFT SETUP:

Even though it's scary to start something new...I'm afraid I'm not ready...I now choose to courageously embrace the new and trust that everything is in Divine Order and I deeply and completely love and accept myself.

MAY 3, 2020

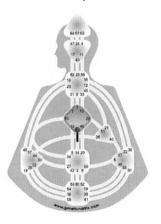

HEXAGRAM 2 - ALLOWING

 ## CHALLENGE:

To love yourself enough to open to the flow of support, love and abundance. To incrementally increase over the course of your life what you're willing to allow yourself to receive. To learn to know that you are valuable and lovable simply because you exist.

JOURNAL QUESTIONS:

1. *Do I ask for help when I need it? Why or why not?*

2. *Do I trust the Universe/God/Spirit/Source to support me in fulfilling my intentions?*

3. Am I grateful for what I have? Make a list of everything I'm grateful for.

4. Can I transform my worry into trust?

5. Do I believe that I deserve to be supported?

 AFFIRMATION:

I allow myself to receive the full flow of resources and abundance I need to fully express all of who I am. I recognize that my life is a vital, irreplaceable part of the cosmic tapestry and I receive all that I need because it helps me contribute all that I am.

 **EFT SETUP:**

Even though I'm scared because nothing looks like I thought it would, I now choose to relax, trust and receive the support that I am designed to receive. I know that I will be supported in expressing my True Self and I deeply and completely love and accept myself.

MAY 7, 2020

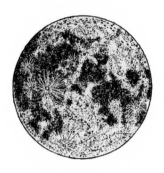

FULL MOON

⏰ 10:45 AM UTC

♏ 17 DEGREES 19 MINUTES SCORPIO

☾ MOON IN GATE 1

Full moon energy invites us to explore what we need to release and let go of in order to stay in alignment with our intentions.

Gate 1, the Gate of Purpose, is a powerful energy that can feel like pressure on your soul. If you feel unclear about your life or soul purpose, this energy can feel like panic. You might find this week that you feel like you're here for a purpose, but if you don't know what that purpose is, you may feel lost or confused.

This is the kind of energy that can cause you to question the meaning of life and can leave you feeling despair and in search of what to *do*.

This energy comes of the Calibration Center, the Center for love, direction and identity. What we are learning this week is that your true life purpose is *not* what you do, but who you are. *You* are the contribution you are here to give the world. Your life story and the authentic fulfillment of who you are is the gift you bring to the planet. Be yourself. Be unapologetically and authentically yourself and your life's path will line up accordingly.

JOURNAL QUESTIONS:

1. *Am I fully expressing my authentic self?*

2. *What needs to be healed, released, aligned or brought to my awareness for me to more deeply express my authentic self?*

3. *Where am I already expressing who I am?*

4. *Where have I settled or compromised? What needs to change?*

5. *Do I feel connected to my life purpose? What do I need to do to deepen that connection?'*

 AFFIRMATION:

My life is an integral part of the cosmos and the Divine Plan. I honor my life and know that the full expression of who I am is the purpose of my life. The more I am who I am, the more I create a frequency of energy that supports others in doing the same. I commit to exploring all of who I am.

MAY 9, 2020

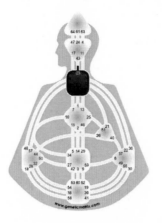

HEXAGRAM 23 - TRANSMISSION

 CHALLENGE:

To recognize that change and transformation are inevitable. To know what needs to happen next, to wait for the right timing and the right people to share your insights with. To not jump the gun and try to convince people to understand what you know. To not let yourself slip into negativity and despair when people aren't ready.

 JOURNAL QUESTIONS:

1. *How can I strengthen my connection to Source?*

2. *Do I trust what I know? What comes up for me when I <u>know</u> something but I don't know how I know what I know?*

3. How do I handle myself when I know something but the people around me aren't ready to hear it yet?

 AFFIRMATION:

I change the world with what I know. My insights and awarenesses have the ability to transform the way people think and perceive the world. I know that my words are powerful and transformative. I trust that the people who are ready for the change that I bring will ask me for what I know. I am a vessel for my knowingness and I nurture myself while I wait to share what I know.

 **EFT SETUP:**

Even though in the past I shut down my voice, I now speak my truth and offer the contribution of my unique spirit to the world and I deeply and completely love and accept myself.

MAY 15, 2020

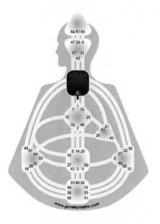

HEXAGRAM 8 - FULFILLMENT

 ## CHALLENGE:

The learn to express yourself authentically. To wait for the right people to see the value of who you are and to share yourself with them, with vulnerability and all of your heart. To learn to trust that you are a unique expression of the Divine with a purpose and a path. To find that path and to walk it without self-judgement or holding back.

 ## JOURNAL QUESTIONS:

1. Do I feel safe being vulnerable? What experiences have caused me to feel unsafe expressing my true self? Can I rewrite those stories?

2. What would an uncompromising life look like for me?

3. What do I need to remove from my current life to make my life more authentic?

4. What is one bold action I can take right now that would allow me to express who I am more authentically in the world? What is my true passion? What do I dream of?

 AFFIRMATION:

I am devoted to the full expression of who I am. I defend and protect the story of my Life. I know that when I am expressing myself, without hesitation or limitation, I AM the contribution that I am here to give the world. Being myself IS my life purpose and my direction flows from my authentic alignment.

 EFT SETUP:

Even though I question whether I have something of value to add to the world, I now choose to courageously follow the whispers of my soul and live a life that is a powerful expression of the truth of who I am. I speak my truth. I value my contribution. I know I am precious and I deeply and completely love and accept myself.

MAY 21, 2020

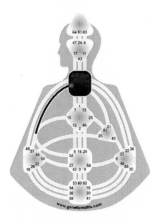

HEXAGRAM 20 - PATIENCE

 ## CHALLENGE:

To be patient and master the ability to wait. To be prepared and watchful but resist the urge to act if the timing isn't right or if there are details that still need to be readied.

 ## JOURNAL QUESTIONS:

1. *How do I manage my need for action? Am I patient? Do I trust in Divine Timing?*

2. *Do I trust my intuition?*

3. What needs to be healed, released, aligned and brought to my awareness for me to trust my intuition?

4. What needs to be healed, released, aligned and brought to my awareness for me to trust my intuition?

💗 AFFIRMATION:

I am in the flow of perfect timing. I listen to my intuition. I prepare. I gather the experience, resources and people I need to support my ideas and my principles. When I am ready, I wait patiently, knowing that right timing is the key to transforming the world. My alignment with right timing increases my influence and my power.

🖐 EFT SETUP:

Even though it's scary to not *do* anything and wait, I now choose to trust the infinite abundance of the Universe and I deeply and completely love and accept myself.

MAY 22, 2020

NEW MOON

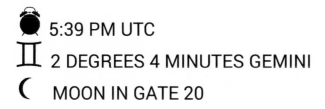

5:39 PM UTC

2 DEGREES 4 MINUTES GEMINI

MOON IN GATE 20

New moon energy invites us to explore how we can deepen our alignment with our intentions and asks us to focus on what we want to grow and expand on in our lives.

Gate 20, the Gate of Patience, invites us into an exploration of our relationship with time and timing.

We are asked by the Sun to deepen our trust in our intuition, to know what needs to be set in place, what people need to be gathered, what skills need to be mastered and to be ready for whatever we are creating when the time is right.

We are invited to explore our relationship with Divine Order and to gauge how much we, not only trust ourselves, but trust in Source and to act as if our intentions are being made manifest, even when we don't see the immediate evidence. We are preparing and waiting for the cosmic signal to take action when the timing is right.

And we're learning to rest and stay aligned in the meantime…

JOURNAL QUESTIONS:

1. *How do I manage my need for action? Am I patient? Do I trust in Divine Timing?*

2. *Do I trust my intuition?*

3. *What needs to be healed, released, aligned and brought to my awareness for me to trust my intuition?*

4. *What needs to be healed, released, aligned and brought to your awareness for me to trust my intuition?*

 AFFIRMATION:

I am in the flow of perfect timing. I listen to my intuition. I prepare. I gather the experience, resources and people I need to support my ideas and my principles. When I am ready, I wait patiently, knowing that right timing is the key to transforming the world. My alignment with right timing increases my influence and my power.

MAY 27, 2020

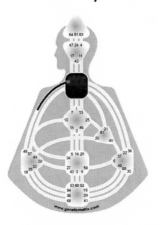

HEXAGRAM 16 - ZEST

 CHALLENGE:

To learn to temper your enthusiasm by making sure you're prepared enough for whatever it is you're trying to do or create.

 JOURNAL QUESTIONS:

1. Do I trust my _gut_?

2. Do I need to slow down and make sure I've done my _homework_ before I take action?

3. Have I sidelined my enthusiasm because other people have told me that I _can't_ do what I'm dreaming of doing?

AFFIRMATION:

I am a faith-filled contagious force. I take guided actions and I trust my intuition and awareness to let me know when I am prepared and ready to leap into expanding my experience and mastery. My enthusiasm inspires others to trust in themselves and to take their own giant leaps of growth.

 ## EFT SETUP:

Even though I'm afraid that I'm not fulfilling my life purpose and I'm wasting my life, I now choose to relax and know that I am in the perfect place at the perfect time to fulfill my destiny and I deeply and completely love and accept myself.

JUNE 1, 2020

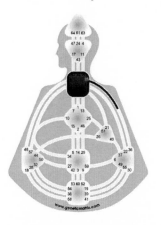

HEXAGRAM 35 - EXPERIENCE

 CHALLENGE:

To not let experience lead to feeling jaded or bored. To have the courage to share what you know from your experience. To know which experiences are worth participating in. To let your natural ability to master anything keep you from being enthusiastic about learning something new. To embrace that even though you know how to know, you don't know everything.

 JOURNAL QUESTIONS:

1. Where am I finding passion in my life? Do I need to create or discover more passion in my life right now?

2. Do I share my knowledge and the stories of my experiences? Do I see the value of what I have to share?

3. *What am I curious about? How can I expand on that curiosity?*

 AFFIRMATION:

I am an experienced, wise and knowledgeable resource for others. My experiences in life have added to the rich tapestry that is the story of Humanity. I share my stories with others because my experiences open doorways of possibility for others. My stories help others create miracles in their lives.

 EFT SETUP:

Even though in the past I struggled to stay focused and move forward, I now trust myself to take the next steps on manifesting my dream. I am focused, clear and moving forward and I deeply and completely love and accept myself.

JUNE 5, 2020

PENUMBRAL LUNAR ECLIPSE

🕐 7:12 PM UTC

♏ 15 DEGREES 33 MINUTES Sagittarius

☾ MOON IN GATE 5

Full Moon – Gate 5 on June 5 at 7:12 PM UTC 15 degrees 33 minutes Sagittarius (Penumbral Lunar Eclipse)

Full moon energy invites us to explore what we need to release and let go of in order to stay in alignment with our intentions.

This is the second in a series of lunar eclipses. The first one was on January 10 in Gate 53, the Gate of Starting. We *complete* this lunar eclipse cycle with the moon in Gate 5, the Gate of Consistency.

We've been exploring over the months the inner question of what do we really want to start in our lives. This has been a celestial season of big disruption and upheaval and it may have hit some of you pretty hard. This cycle of change has been an invitation to explore what else you'd like to create in your life. With old patterns being disrupted and old paradigms dismantled, it's time to start fresh.

Gate 5 demands of us to give our dreams and intentions consistent energy and focus. We are encouraged now to buckle down and get to work building what we really want in our lives. Even if it seems like everything has been torn down to the foundation, we're rebuilding with greater clarity and a deeper intention to create more resources and the capacity to live from the Heart. What habits do you need to maintain and cultivate to sustain your renewed intentions and focus?

JOURNAL QUESTIONS:

1. What do I need to do to create habits that fuel my energy and keep me vital and feeling connected to myself and Source?

2. What habits do I have that might not be serving my highest expression? How can I change those habits?

3. What kind of environment do I need to cultivate to support my rhythmic nature?

 AFFIRMATION:

Consistency gives me power. When I am aligned with my own natural rhythm and the rhythm of life around me I cultivate strength, connection with Source and I am a beacon of stability and order. The order I hold is the touchstone, the returning point of love, that is sustained through cycles of change. The rhythms I maintain set the standard for compassionate action in the world.

JUNE 7, 2020

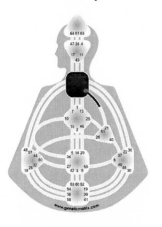

HEXAGRAM 45 - DISPENSATION

 ## CHALLENGE:

To share and use your resources for the greater good of the whole. To learn to manage resources judiciously so that they benefit the most amount of people. To teach as a pathway of sharing.

 ## JOURNAL QUESTIONS:

1. Do I like to share? What do I have to give the world?

2. How do I own my right leadership? Am I comfortable as a leader? Do I shrink from leadership? Do I overcompensate by pushing too hard with my leadership?

3. Do I trust that when the right people are ready I will be pressed into action as a leader and a teacher? What do I need to heal, release, align or bring to my awareness to trust my leadership energy more?

 # AFFIRMATION:

I am a teacher and a leader. I use my resources, my knowledge and my experience to expand the resources, knowledge and experiences of others. I use my blessings of abundance to increase the blessings of others. I know that I am a vehicle of wisdom and knowledge. I sense when it's right for me to share who I am and what I know with others.

 # EFT SETUP:

Even though I'm afraid to look at my finances, I now choose to take a real look at my financial numbers and know that awareness is the first step to increasing my financial status and I deeply and completely love and accept myself.

JUNE 13, 2020

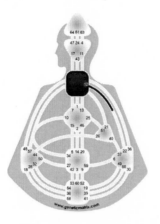

HEXAGRAM 12 - THE CHANNEL

 CHALLENGE:

To honor the self enough to wait for the right time and *mood* to speak. To know that *shyness* is actually a signal that the timing isn't right to share your transformational insights and expressions. When the timing IS right, to have the courage to share what you feel and sense. To honor the fact that your voice and the words you offer are a direct connection to Source and you channel the potential for transformation. To own your creative power.

 JOURNAL QUESTIONS:

1. *How has <u>shyness</u> caused me to judge myself?*

2. *What do I need to do to cultivate a deeper connection with Source?*

3. *What do I need to do to connect more deeply with my creative power?*

 ## AFFIRMATION:

I am a creative being. My words, my self-expression, my creative offerings have the power to change the way people see and understand the world. I am a vessel of Divine Transformation and I serve Source through the words that I share. I wait for the right timing and when I am aligned with timing and flow, my creativity creates beauty and Grace in the world. I am a Divine Channel and I trust that the words that I serve will open the Hearts of others.

 ## EFT SETUP:

Even though I'm afraid that I'm failing my life purpose and mission, I now choose to know that I am in the right place fulfilling my right purpose. All I need to do is to follow my strategy, be deliberate, follow my heart and all will be exactly as it needs to be and I deeply and completely love and accept myself.

JUNE 19, 2020

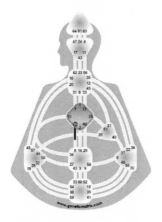

HEXAGRAM 15 - COMPASSION

 CHALLENGE:

To learn to allow yourself to be in the flow of your own rhythm. To not beat yourself up because you don't have daily *habits*. To have the courage to do the right thing even if you are worried about not having enough. To share from the Heart without giving up your Heart and serving as a *martyr*.

 JOURNAL QUESTIONS:

1. Do I trust my own rhythm?

2. Do I share from the Heart? Do I over share? Does my sharing compromise my own Heart?

3. Do I judge my own rhythm? Can I find peace in aligning with my own rhythm?

4. What old patterns do I need to break?

 ## AFFIRMATION:

Like the power of a hurricane to transform the shoreline, my unique rhythm brings change to the landscape of my life and the world around me. I embrace my own rhythm and acknowledge the power of my own Heart. I share with ease and I serve my own Heart as the foundation of all I have to give the world.

 ## EFT SETUP:

Even though I feel powerless to make a difference in the world, I now choose to follow my heart and my passion knowing that I am the greatest gift I can give the world. The more I show up as my true self, the more I empower others to do the same and I deeply and completely love and accept myself.

JUNE 21, 2020

ANNUAL SOLAR ECLIPSE

 06:42 AM UTC

 0 DEGREES 21 MINUTES CANCER

☾ MOON IN GATE 15

New Moon – Gate 15 on June 21 at 06:42 AM UTC 0 degrees 21 minutes Cancer

Annual Solar Eclipse, Sun in Gate 15

Solar eclipses are always Cosmic Turning points, a powerful time of reprogramming your essential life force to align with your Authentic Self. We are invited to explore whether our outer reality and the way in which we are living is an accurate mirror of who we know ourselves to truly be, our authentic cosmic identities.

Gate 15, the Gate of Compassion, shows us that the natural human response to extreme cycles of change, especially cataclysmic ones, is compassion. When disaster or extreme events happen, we are able to reach out across the perceptions that create barriers of separation and find the commonalities between our human Hearts.

This energy promises to shake up those places where you may be stuck in a rut. You may find yourself suddenly having to navigate the unexpected or to reach out to others who are feeling shocked and rocked by life.

The energy of compassion lies on the Calibration Center, the Center that gives direction to Love and our Hearts. We see that when we respond to each other with compassion we actually raise our frequency and vibration, and increase what we allow ourselves to attract into our life. This can be an extreme cycle of expansion of goodness. This energy allows us to explore how much we want to share and encourages us to trust Source enough to share from an abundant spirit and a mindset of sufficiency.

Be prepared for massive change with this eclipse and to wake up to a bigger awareness of what we need to do to create alignment between the people in our lives and the people of the planet.

 JOURNAL QUESTIONS:

1. Do I trust my own rhythm?

2. Do I share from the Heart? Do I over share? Does my sharing compromise my own Heart?

3. Do I judge my own rhythm? Can I find peace in aligning with my own rhythm?

4. What old patterns do I need to break?

 AFFIRMATION:

Like the power of a hurricane to transform the shoreline, my unique rhythm brings change to the landscape of my life and the world around me. I embrace my own rhythm and acknowledge the power of my own Heart. I share with ease and I serve my own Heart as the foundation of all I have to give the world.

JUNE 25, 2020

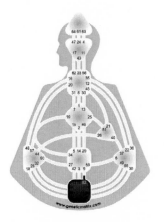

HEXAGRAM 52 - PERSPECTIVE

 CHALLENGE:

To learn to stay focused even when you're overwhelmed by a bigger perspective. To see the "big picture", to not let the massive nature of what you know confuse you and cause you to struggle with where to put your energy and attention.

 JOURNAL QUESTIONS:

1. What do I do to maintain and sustain my focus? Is there anything in my environment or my life that I need to move out of the way in order for me to deepen my focus?

2. How do I manage feeling overwhelmed? What things am I avoiding because I feel overwhelmed by them? What is one bold action I can take to begin clearing the path for action?

3. How does my feeling of being overwhelmed affect my self-worth? How can I love myself more deeply in spite of feeling overwhelmed?

 ## AFFIRMATION:

I am like the eagle soaring above the land. I see the entirety of what needs to happen to facilitate the evolution of the world. I use my perspective to see my unique and irreplaceable role in the Cosmic Plan. I see relationships and patterns that others don't always see. My perspective helps us all to build a peaceful world more effectively and in a consciously directed way.

 ## EFT SETUP:

Even though it makes me nervous to stop "doing" and sit with the stillness, I now trust the process and know that my state of alignment and clarity with my intentions is the most powerful thing I can do to create effectively and powerfully in my life. I relax, I trust and let my abundance unfold and I deeply and completely love and accept myself.

JULY 1, 2020

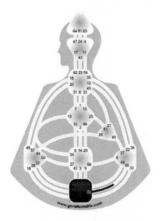

HEXAGRAM 39 - RE-CALIBRATION

 CHALLENGE:

To challenge and tease out energies that are not in alignment with faith and abundance. To bring them to awareness and to use them as pushing off points to deepen faith and trust in Source.

 JOURNAL QUESTIONS:

1. *Do I trust Source? What do I need to do to deepen my trust in Source?*

2. *Do I feel like I am <u>enough</u>? Do I feel like I have <u>enough</u>?*

3. Take stock of everything I have and everything I've been given. Do I have enough? Have I ever really not been supported?

4. What do I have that I'm grateful for?

5. Have I abdicated my own power to create? What needs to be healed, released, aligned or brought to my awareness to reactivate my power to create my own abundance?

AFFIRMATION:

I am deeply calibrated with my faith. I trust that I am fully supported. I use experiences that create desire and wanting in me as opportunities to deepen my faith that I will receive and create all that I need to fulfill my mind, body and spirit. I am in the perfect flow of abundance and I am deeply aligned with Source.

✋ EFT SETUP.

Even though I worry about money, having the right relationship, and creating abundance in every area of my life, I now trust Spirit and allow the abundant nature of the Universe to reveal itself to me. I stay open to the possibilities of miracles and trust that all I have to do is stay conscious of the abundance of Spirit unfolding within me and I deeply and completely love and accept myself.

JULY 5, 2020

PENUMBRAL LUNAR ECLIPSE

 04:44 AM UTC

 13 DEGREES 37 MINUTES CAPRICORN

☾ MOON IN GATE 38

Full Moon – Gate 38 on July 5 at 04:44 AM UTC 13 degrees 37 minutes Capricorn (penumbral Lunar Eclipse)

Full moon energy invites us to explore what we need to release and let go of in order to stay in alignment with our intentions.

Gate 38, the Gate of the Visionary, is pushing us to examine what we really think is worth committing to in our lives. This is the energy that helps us keep our "eye on the prize" and with this energy we are exploring what is truly valuable and meaningful in our lives. We're looking at whether we are living in alignment with our values and the priorities of our Heart and if we find that we could use some improvement here. We are being supported in making sure that our actions, our Hearts and our intentions line up.

What do you need to let go of and release to streamline your purpose and your vision?

JOURNAL QUESTIONS:

1. *Do I know what's worth committing to and fighting for in my life?*

2. *Do I have a dream that I am sharing with the world?*

3. *Do I know how to use my struggles and challenges as the catalyst for creating deeper meaning in the world? In my life?*

 AFFIRMATION:

My challenges, struggles and adventures have taught me about what is truly valuable in life. I use my understanding to hold a vision of what else is possible for the world. I am aligned with the values that reflect the preciousness of life and I sustain a vision for a world that is aligned with Heart. My steadfast commitment to my vision inspires others to join me in creating a world of equitable, sustainable peace.

JULY 7, 2020

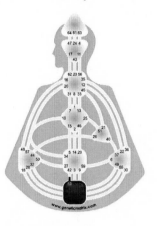

HEXAGRAM 53 - STARTING

 CHALLENGE:

To respond in alignment with your energy blueprint to opportunities to get things started. To initiate the process of preparing or "setting the state" for the manifestation of a dream before it becomes a reality. To learn to trust in the timing of the Universe and not take charge and try to implement your own ideas while working against Divine Timing. To not burn out trying to complete things. To find peace as a "starter," not a "finisher."

 JOURNAL QUESTIONS:

1. How do I feel about myself when I have an idea and I can't get it initiated?

2. How do I feel when someone takes my initial idea and builds on it? Do I value what I started?

3. What identities and attachments do I have to being the one who starts and finishes something?

4. Do I judge myself for not finishing something? How can I be more gentle with myself?

5. Do I trust Divine Timing? How can I deepen my trust in right timing?

 AFFIRMATION:

I am a servant to Divine Inspiration. My thoughts, inspirations and ideas set the stage for creative expansion and the potential for evolution. I take action on the ideas that present themselves to me in an aligned way. I honor all other ideas knowing that my gift is in the spark of energy that gets things rolling when the timing is right. While I wait for right timing, I guard my energy and charge my battery so that I am sustainable when the time is right for action.

 EFT SETUP:

Even though I'm scared to believe that my big dreams could come true, I now choose to trust the infinite power of the Universe and know that I am never given a dream that can't be fulfilled.

JULY 13, 2020

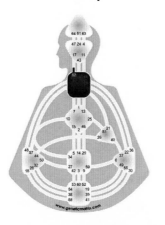

HEXAGRAM 62 - PREPARATION

 CHALLENGE:

To trust that you'll be prepared for the next step. To not let worry and over-preparation detract you from being present in the moment. To let the fear of not being ready keep you trapped.

 JOURNAL QUESTIONS:

1. Do I worry? What do I do to manage my worry?

2. What can I do to trust that I know what I need to know? What proof do I have that I am in the flow of preparation?

3. Is there anything in my life right now that I need to plan for? Am I over-planning? Does my need for contingency plans keep me stuck?

 AFFIRMATION:

I create the foundation for the practice of mastery by engineering the plan of action that creates growth. I am in the flow of my understanding and I use my knowledge and experience to be prepared for the evolution of what's next. I am ready and I am prepared. I trust my own preparation and allow myself to be in the flow of what's next knowing that I'll know what I need to know when I need to know it.

EFT SETUP:

Even though I feel pressure to do something, I now choose to relax and trust the power of my dreams to call the right circumstance to me and I deeply and completely love and accept myself.

JULY 19, 2019

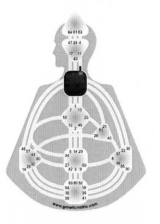

HEXAGRAM 56 - EXPANSION

 **CHALLENGE:**

To learn to share stories and inspirations with the right people at the right time. To learn to tell stories of expansion and not depletion and contraction.

 JOURNAL QUESTIONS:

1. What stories do I share repeatedly with others? Do they lift people up or cause them to contract?

2. What stories do I tell about myelf and my voice that cause me to either expand or contract?

3. *What am I here to inspire others to do or be?*

 ## AFFIRMATION:

I am a Divine Storyteller. The stories of possibility that I share have the power to inspire others to grow and expand. I use my words as a template for possibility and expansion for the world. I inspire the world with my words.

 ## EFT SETUP:

Even though I'm afraid to share my ideas, I now choose to take leadership with my inspirations and share my precious ideas with others and I deeply and completely love and accept myself.

JULY 20, 2020

NEW MOON

 5:33 PM UTC

 28 DEGREES 26 MINUTES CANCER

☾ MOON IN GATE 56

New moon energy invites us to explore how we can deepen our alignment with our intentions and asks us to focus on what we want to grow and expand on in our lives.

Gate 56, the Gate of Expansion, is the energy that helps us use the power of storytelling to rewrite the personal narrative we tell about our experiences in life. This is the energy that helps us create "alter egos" and "super powers" to spark in us a new frequency of possibility in our reality. When we work with this energy we are encouraged to use the power of story telling to expand upon what our logical mind is telling us is possible. This energy pushes you past the limitations of logic and invites you to contemplate what else is possible for you and your life.

What stories are you telling that may be limiting your ability to align with something bigger than what you're living right now? Where is your mind limiting your willingness to engage in possibility thinking and shutting down your imagination and dreaming?

JOURNAL QUESTIONS:

1. What stories do I share repeatedly with others? Do they lift people up or cause them to contract?

2. What stories do I tell about myself and my voice that cause me to either expand or contract?

3. What am I here to inspire others to do or be?

 AFFIRMATION:

I am a Divine Storyteller. The stories of possibility that I share have the power to inspire others to grow and expand. I use my words as a template for possibility and expansion for the world. I inspire the world with my words.

JULY 24, 2020

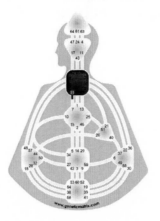

HEXAGRAM 31 - THE LEADER

 ## CHALLENGE:

To learn to lead as a representative of the people you are leading. To cultivate a leadership agenda of service. To not let your fear of not being seen, heard or accepted get in the way of healthy leadership. To learn to take your rightful place as a leader and not hide out.

 ## JOURNAL QUESTIONS:

1. How do I feel about being a leader? Am I comfortable leading? Do I shrink from taking leadership?

2. What is my place of service? Who do I serve?

AFFIRMATION:

I am a natural born leader. I serve at my highest potential when I am empowering others by giving them a voice and then serving their needs. I use my power to lead people to a greater expansion of who they are and to support them in increasing their abundance, sustainability and peace.

 EFT SETUP:

Even though I'm afraid to be seen, I now choose to express myself and the magnificence that is me with gusto, courage, awareness of my own power and preciousness and I deeply and completely love and accept myself.

JULY 30, 2020

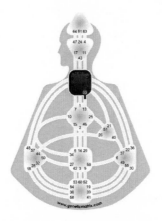

HEXAGRAM 33 - RETELLING

 ## CHALLENGE:

To learn to share a personal narrative that reflects your true value and your worth. To share a personal narrative when it serves the intention to serve, improving the direction of others. To share history in an empowering way.

 ## JOURNAL QUESTIONS:

1. What personal narratives am I telling that might be keeping me stuck, feeling like a victim or feeling unlovable? How can I rewrite these stories?

2. What listening practices do I have? What can I do to listen better so that I can gauge when it is the right time to share in a powerful way?

AFFIRMATION:

I am a processor of stories. My gift is my ability to help others find the blessings, the love and the power from stories of pain. I hold people's secrets and stories and transform them to share when the time is right. The stories I tell change the direction of people's lives. I use the power of stories to increase the power of Heart in the world and to help build a world of Love.

 ## EFT SETUP:

Even though my stories from my past have held me back, I now choose to rewrite the story of my life and tell it the way I choose, with forgiveness, embracing the gifts and honoring my courage and strength in my story and I deeply and completely love and accept myself.

AUGUST 3, 2020

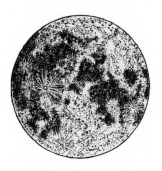

FULL MOON

3:59 PM UTC

11 DEGREES 45 MINUTES AQUARIUS

MOON IN GATE 19

Full moon energy invites us to explore what we need to release and let go of in order to stay in alignment with our intentions.

Gate 19, the Gate of Attunement, brings us an energy of sensitivity and awareness of what needs to change in our relationships and emotional environment to bring us closer and to create greater intimacy and connection.

When we work with this energy we are encouraged to take stock of our relationships and to explore whether they are in alignment with our values and desires. Are you getting what you want and need in your partnerships? If not, is it time to make some changes? If you are, what can you grow and deepen to make the bonds that tie you even stronger?

The environment you place yourself in, the energy of your relationships and your community influences your own emotional energy tremendously. A supportive and nurturing environment increases your sustainability and your creative capacity. Being in strong and uplifting partnerships is crucial for sustaining and growing your faith and can actually change the way you experience time and timing. It's much easier to wait and time goes by faster when you feel loved and supported.

JOURNAL QUESTIONS:

1. How do I manage my sensitivity? What coping mechanism do I have that keep me emotionally connected in a healthy way?

2. Am I emotionally present in my relationships? Do I need to become more attuned to my own emotional needs and ask for more of what I want and need?

3. What emotional patterns do I have that may be causing me to give up what I need and want to fulfill other people's emotional needs?

4. Am I able to be present in the emotional energy around me to help calibrate in a creative, intimate and sustainable way?

 AFFIRMATION:

I am deeply aware of the emotional needs and energy of others. My sensitivity and awareness gives me insights that allow me to create intimacy and vulnerability in my relationships. I am aware and attuned to the emotional frequency around me and I make adjustments to help support a high frequency of emotional alignment. I honor my own emotional needs as the foundation of what I share with others.

AUGUST 5, 2020

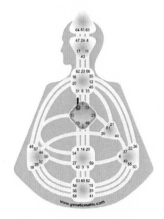

HEXAGRAM 7 - COLLABORATOR

 CHALLENGE:

To master the need to be in front and allow yourself to serve through building teams, collaborating and influencing the figurehead of leadership. To be at peace with serving the leader through support and collaboration. To recognize that the voice of the leader is only as strong and powerful as the support he/she receives.

 JOURNAL QUESTIONS:

1. What are my gifts and strengths? How do I use those gifts to influence and lead others?

2. How do I feel about not being the figurehead of leadership? What happens when I only support the leadership? Do I still feel powerful? Influential?

3. *Make a list of the times when my influence has positively directed leadership?*

 ## AFFIRMATION:

I am an agent of peace who influences the direction and organization of leadership. I unify people around ideas. I influence with my wisdom, my knowledge and my connections. I am a team builder, a collaborator and I organize people in ways that empower them and support them in creating a collective direction rooted in compassion.

 ## EFT SETUP:

Even though I feel confused and conflicted about what to do, I trust the Divine Flow and let the Universe show me the right thing to do in the right time and I deeply and completely love, trust and accept myself.

AUGUST 11, 2020

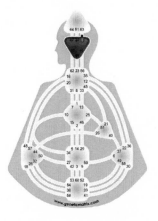

HEXAGRAM 4 - POSSIBILITY

 CHALLENGE:

To learn to embrace ideas as possibilities, not answers, and to let the power of the possibility stimulate the imagination as a way of calibrating the emotions and the Heart. This Gate teaches us the power of learning to wait to see which possibility actually manifests in the physical world and to experiment with options in response.

 JOURNAL QUESTIONS:

1. *What ideas do I have right now that need me to nurture and activate them?*

2. *What possibilities do these ideas stimulate right now? Take some time to write or visualize the possibilities.*

3. Am I comfortable with waiting? What can I do to increase my patience and curiosity?

 ## AFFIRMATION:

I am tuned into the cosmic flow of possibility. I am inspired about exploring new possibilities and potentials. I use the power of my thoughts to stretch the limits of what is known and engage my imagination to explore the potential of the unknown.

 ## EFT SETUP:

Even though I don't know what to do, I allow my questions to seed the Universe and I trust and wait with great patience that the answers will be revealed to me and I deeply and completely love and accept myself.

AUGUST 17, 2020

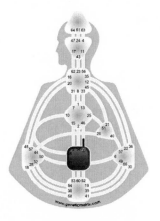

HEXAGRAM 29 - DEVOTION

 ## CHALLENGE:

To discover what and who you need to devote yourself to. To sustain yourself so that you can sustain your devotion. To learn to say "no" to what you need to say "no" to and to learn to "yes" to what you want to say "yes" to.

 ## JOURNAL QUESTIONS:

1. What devotion do I have right now that drives me? Is this a devotion that inspires me or do I feel overly obligated to it?

2. Who would I be and what would I choose if I gave myself permission to say "no" more often?

3. What would I like to say "no" to that I am saying "yes" to right now?

4. What obligations do I need to take off my plate right now?

5. What would I like to devote myself to?

 ## AFFIRMATION:

I have an extraordinary ability to devote myself to the manifestation of an idea. My commitment to my story and to the fulfillment of my intention changes the story of what's possible in my own life and for humanity. I choose my commitments with great care. I devote myself to what's vital for the evolution of the world and I nurture myself first because my well-being is the foundation of what I create.

 ## EFT SETUP:

Even though I'm afraid to invest all my effort into my dream...what if it fails...what if I'm crazy...what if I just need to buckle down and be "normal"...I now choose to do it anyway and I deeply and completely love and accept myself.

AUGUST 19, 2020

NEW MOON

 02:42 AM UTC

 26 DEGREES 34 MINUTES LEO

☾ MOON IN GATE 29

New moon energy invites us to explore how we can deepen our alignment with our intentions and asks us to focus on what we want to grow and expand on in our lives.

Gate 29, the Gate of Devotion, brings us opportunity to explore our level of commitment and devotion to the fulfillment of our intentions. This is a tantric energy in Human Design, an energy that is about doing the work to express your mastery and embody the essence of who you are. It's the energy of discipline and commitment that yields results over time.

You are being invited by the planets this week to explore your commitments and your practices. Are you devoted to your right work and your purpose in the world. This energy is best represented in the story of the Olympic athlete who rises before the sun for years to train and fine tune their skills. We love the story of the athlete because we are all, on some level, metaphorical athletes.

With this energy matched with the initiating power of the new moon, it's time to renew your commitment to whatever it is you're creating in the world. Do you need to change your level of commitment, cultivate a better practice in order to deepen your skill set and do whatever it is that you set out to do?

JOURNAL QUESTIONS:

1. What devotion do I have right now that drives me? Is this a devotion that inspires me or do I feel overly obligated to it?

2. Who would I be and what I choose if I gave myself permission to say "no" more often?

3. What would I like to say "no" to that I am saying "yes" to right now?

4. What obligations do I need to take off my plate right now?

5. What would I like to devote myself to?

 AFFIRMATION:

I have an extraordinary ability to devote myself to the manifestation of an idea. My commitment to my story and to the fulfillment of my intention changes the story of what's possible in my own life and for humanity. I choose my commitments with great care. I devote myself to what's vital for the evolution of the world and I nurture myself first because my well-being is the foundation of what I create.

AUGUST 23, 2020

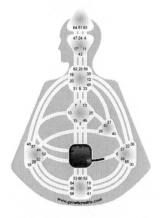

HEXAGRAM 59 - SUSTAINABILITY

 **CHALLENGE:**

To learn to make abundant choices that sustain you, and at the same time, others. To collaborate and initiate others into sustainable relationships from a place of sufficiency. To learn to share what you have in a sustainable way.

 JOURNAL QUESTIONS:

1. *Do I trust in my own abundance?*

2. *How do I feel about sharing what I have with others?*

3. *Am I creating relationship and partnership agreements that honor my work?*

4. *Do I have relationships and agreements that are draining me? What needs to change?*

5. *How do I feel about being "right"? Am I open to other ways of thinking or being? Do I believe in creating agreements and alignments with people who have different values and perspectives?*

 ## AFFIRMATION:

The energy that I carry has the power to create sufficiency and sustainability for all. I craft valuable alliances and agreements that support me in expanding abundance for everyone. I hold to higher principles and values that are rooted in my trust in sufficiency and the all-providing Source. Through my work and alignments my blessings serve to increase the blessings of myself and others.

 ## EFT SETUP:

Even though I struggle to share my intentions, I now choose to boldly state my intentions and wait for the pieces of my creation to magically fall into place and I deeply and completely love and accept myself.

AUGUST 29, 2020

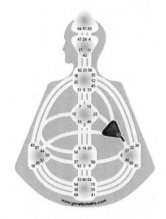

HEXAGRAM 40 - RESTORATION

 CHALLENGE:

To learn to value yourself enough to retreat from community and the energy of those you love to restore, restock and replenish your inner resources. To learn to interpret the signal of loneliness correctly. To take responsibility for your own care and resources and to not abdicate your own power to take care of yourself.

 JOURNAL QUESTIONS:

1. *What role does loneliness play in my life? Has loneliness caused me to doubt my value?*

2. *What do I need to do to restore my energy? Am I doing enough to take care of myself?*

3. What agreements am I making in my relationships that might be causing me to compromise my value? How can I rewrite these agreements?

4. Am I abdicating my responsibility for my self-care? Am I living a "martyr" model? What needs to be healed, released, aligned and brought to my awareness for me to take responsibility for cultivating my own sense of value and my self-worth?

 AFFIRMATION:

I am a powerful resource for my community. The energy that I hold impacts others deeply and brings them to deeper states of alignment and sustainability. I take care of my body, mind and soul because I know that the more that I am and the more that I have, the more I can give to others. I take care of myself first because I know that good things flow from me. I am valuable and powerful and I claim and defend the true story of Who I Truly Am.

 EFT SETUP:

Even though it is hard to let go of the obligations of relationships, I now choose to release all relationships that are draining and unsupportive and I deeply and completely love and accept myself.

SEPTEMBER 2, 2020

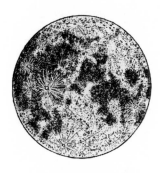

FULL MOON

⏰ 05:23 AM UTC

♓ 10 DEGREES 11 MINUTES PISCES

☾ MOON IN GATE 37

Full moon energy invites us to explore what we need to release and let go of in order to stay in alignment with our intentions.

Gate 37, the Gate of Harmony, is giving us the energy to explore what needs to be released and aligned in our lives to support us in cultivating a deeper level of peace. To create peace in our lives and in the world, we have to first cultivate inner peace.

With the full moon inviting us to let go and release, we are exploring what we need to let go of to create a deeper state of peace. Are there things in your environment that are disturbing your inner peace? Do you need to adjust your patterns and habits to support your practice of creating inner peace?

This is an emotional energy. When we are aligned with peace we create sustainable solutions to the challenges facing our every day life. When we struggle with inner peace, we react and have the potential to feel embattled or to fight. Inner peace increases our creativity and flow.

JOURNAL QUESTIONS:

1. What habits, practices and routines do I have that cultivate my inner alignment with sustainable peace?

2. When I feel that my outer world is chaotic and disrupted how do I cultivate inner peace?

3. What do I need to do to cultivate a peaceful emotional frequency?

 AFFIRMATION:

I am an agent of peace. My being aligned with peace creates an energy of contagious peace around me. I practice holding a peaceful frequency of energy and I respond to the world with an intention of creating sustainable peace.

SEPTEMBER 3, 2020

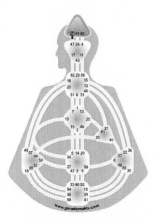

HEXAGRAM 64 - DIVINE TRANSFERENCE

 **CHALLENGE:**

To not let the power of your big ideas overwhelm you and shut down your dreaming and creating. To not get lost in the pressure of answering the question "how."

 JOURNAL QUESTIONS:

1. *What do I do to take care of my Big Ideas?*

2. *How do I feel about having "dreams" but not always the solutions?*

3. *How can I stop judging the gift of my dreams?*

4. Do I trust that the "how" of my ideas will be revealed? How can I deepen this trust?

 AFFIRMATION:

I am a conduit for expansive thinking. My inspirations and ideas create the seeds of possibility in my mind and in the mind of others. I honor the dreams that pass through my mind and allow my big ideas to stimulate my imagination and the imagination of others. I trust the Universe to reveal the details of my dreams when the time is right. I use the power of my dreams to stimulate a world of possibility and expansion.

EFT SETUP:

Even though I don't know what's next, I wait and trust that the perfect right step will show up for me and I deeply and completely love and accept myself.

Even though I feel overwhelmed with ideas, I trust the Universe to reveal the next step to me. I relax and wait and I deeply and completely love and accept myself.

SEPTEMBER 9, 2020

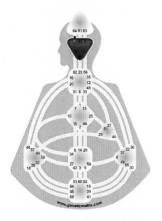

GATE 47 - MINDSET

 CHALLENGE:

To master a mindset of open-ness and possibility. To not let inspiration die because you don't know "how" to fulfill it.

 JOURNAL QUESTIONS:

1. What thoughts do I have when I receive an idea or inspiration? Am I hopeful or despairing? How does it feel to let go of figuring out "how" I'm going to make my idea a reality?

2. What do I do to regulate my mindset? What practices do I need to cultivate to increase the power of my thoughts?

AFFIRMATION:

My mindset is the source of my inspired actions and attitude. I know that when I receive an idea and inspiration it is my job to nurture the idea by using the power of my imagination to increase the potential and emotional frequency of the idea. I consistently keep my inner and outer environment aligned with the energy of possibility and potential. I know that it is my job to create by virtue of my alignment and I relax knowing that it's the job of the Universe to fulfill my inspirations.

 ## EFT SETUP:

Even though it's frustrating to not know how to make something happen, I now choose to wait for Divine Insight and I trust that the right information will be revealed to me at the perfect time and I deeply and completely love and accept myself.

SEPTEMBER 15, 2020

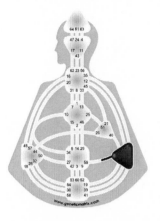

HEXAGRAM 6 - IMPACT

 CHALLENGE:

The ability to master emotional energy and learn to trust that your impact is in service to the world. When you understand that your life is a vehicle for service and your energy is being used to influence and impact those around you, you assume greater obligation and responsibility to maintaining a high frequency of energy. The quality of the emotional energy you cultivate influences others to come together in an equitable, sustainable and peaceful way. Learning to trust that you're words and impact will have effect when the timing is correct and not overriding Divine Timing.

 JOURNAL QUESTIONS:

1. *What do I need to do to deepen my trust in Divine Timing?*

2. *What do I need to do to prepare myself to be seen and to have influence?*

3.   What do I need to do to sustain my emotional energy in order to align with peaceful and sustainable solutions?

4.   How do I feel about lack? How do I feel about abundance? How can I create a greater degree of emotional abundance in my life? In my daily practice?

 **AFFIRMATION:**

My emotional energy influences the world around me. I am rooted in the energy of equity, sustainability and peace. When I am aligned with abundance, I am an energetic source of influence that facilitates elegant solutions to creating peace and well-being. I am deliberate and aligned with values that create peace in my life, in my community and in the world.

✋ EFT SETUP:

Even though I'm ready to leap into action, I now choose to take a breath, wait out my emotions and trust that the right timing will be revealed to me. I'm not missing out on anything. Divine Order is the rule of the day and I deeply and completely love and accept myself.

SEPTEMBER 17, 2020

NEW MOON

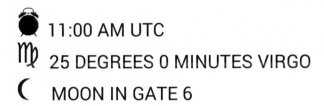

11:00 AM UTC

25 DEGREES 0 MINUTES VIRGO

MOON IN GATE 6

New moon energy invites us to explore how we can deepen our alignment with our intentions and asks us to focus on what we want to grow and expand on in our lives.

The New Moon in Gate 6, the Gate of Impact, invites us to explore how we can increase our impact and service to the world. Your very existence serves the world and this New Moon energy encourages you to explore the relationship between what you have and what you have to give.

When you understand that your life is a vehicle for service and your energy is being used to influence and impact those around you, you assume greater obligation and responsibility to maintaining a high frequency of energy. With the New Moon lighting this energy up this week, we are being asked to explore our perception of our abundance and our alignment with Divine Timing.

When we are feeling abundant and relaxed about Divine Timing, we enter into a creative flow that can impact others in a powerful and peaceful way. With this alignment we see the way and the path to increasing our influence and impact in the world.

JOURNAL QUESTIONS:

1. *What do I need to do to deepen my trust in Divine Timing?*

2. *What do I need to do to prepare myself to be seen and to have influence?*

3. *What do I need to do to sustain my emotional energy in order to align with peaceful and sustainable solutions?*

4. *How do I feel about lack? How do I feel about abundance? How can I create a greater degree of emotional abundance in my life? In my daily practice?*

 AFFIRMATION:

My emotional energy influences the world around me. I am rooted in the energy of equity, sustainability and peace. When I am aligned with abundance, I am an energetic source of influence that facilitates elegant solutions to creating peace and well-being. I am deliberate and aligned with values that create peace in my life, in my community and in the world.

SEPTEMBER 21, 2020

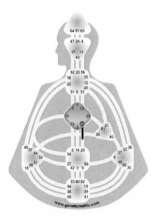

HEXAGRAM 46 - EMBODIMENT

 CHALLENGE:

To learn to love your body. To learn to fully be in your body. To learn to love the sensual nature of your physical form and to move it with love and awareness.

 JOURNAL QUESTIONS:

1. *Do I love my body? What can I do to deepen my love for my body?*

2. *What parts of my body do I love and appreciate? Make a list of every part of my body that I love.*

3. What do I need to do to amplify the life force I am experiencing in my body?

4. What kinds of devotion and commitment do I experience that help me harness greater amounts of life force in my body? How can I deepen my commitment and devotion to my body?

 ## AFFIRMATION:

My body is the vehicle for my soul. My ability to fully express who I am and my life and soul purpose is deeply rooted in my body's ability to carry my soul. I love, nurture and commit to my body. I appreciate all of its miraculous abilities and form. Every day I love my body more.

 ## EFT SETUP:

Even though it's hard for me to love my body, I now choose to embrace my amazing physical form and honor it for all the good it brings me and I deeply and completely love and accept myself.

SEPTEMBER 27, 2020

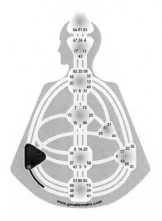

HEXAGRAM 18 - RE-ALIGNMENT

 CHALLENGE:

To learn to wait for the right timing and the right circumstances to offer your intuitive insights into how to fix or correct a pattern. To wait for the right time and the right reason to share your critique. To understand that the purpose of re-alignment is to create more joy, not to be "right".

 JOURNAL QUESTIONS:

1. *What does joy mean to me? How do I serve it?*

2. *How do I cultivate joy in my own life?*

3.   How does it feel to be "right" about something and keep it to myself? Do I need to release any old "stories" about needing to be "right"?

4. Do I trust my own insights? Do I have the courage to share them when it's necessary?

 ## AFFIRMATION:

I am a powerful force that re-aligns patterns. My insights and awareness gives people the information they need to deepen their mastery and to experience greater joy. I serve joy and I align the patterns of the world to increase the world's potential for living in the flow of joy.

 ## EFT SETUP:

Even though I feel criticized and judged, I now choose to hear the wisdom of the correction and release my personal attachment and I deeply and completely love and accept myself.

OCTOBER 1, 2020

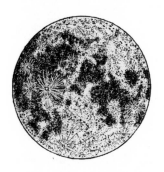

FULL MOON

 9:06 PM UTC

♈ 9 DEGREES 08 MINUTES ARIES

☾ MOON IN GATE 17

Full moon energy invites us to explore what we need to release and let go of in order to stay in alignment with our intentions.

Gate 17, the Gate of Anticipation, can be challenging. We often express this energy as "opinions" and share them in unsolicited ways creating tension and judgement in our relationships. The higher potential of this energy is that it gives us ideas about possibilities that, when the timing is right, are worthy of exploring and experimenting with in order to prove their worthiness.

The energy of Gate 17, gives us clues and cues about what is possible in our lives. It's an expansive energy that invites us to explore what could be next in our lives. This isn't an energy that evokes certainty. It's a call to experiment with ideas that help us prepare for what might be next in our lives.

We are being called to look at past patterns and future disruptions of patterns and to have potential solutions lined up and ready to be explored and implemented.

When you look around at your life, are you staying stuck in old patterns? Are you preparing to adjust to change and expansion? What do you need to do to set the stage for a new cycle of growth in your life?

JOURNAL QUESTIONS:

1.   What do I need to do to manage my insights and ideas so that they increase the options and potential of others?

2. How do I feel about holding back from sharing my insights until the timing is right? What can I do to manage my need to share without waiting for the right timing?

3. What routines and strategies do I need to cultivate to keep my perspectives expanding and possibility oriented?

4. How can I improve my ability to manage doubt and fear?

 AFFIRMATION:

I use the power of my mind to explore possibilities and potential. I know that the inspirations and insights that I have create exploration and experimentation that can inspire the elegant solutions necessary to master the challenges facing humanity.

OCTOBER 2, 2020

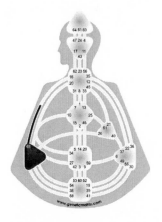

HEXAGRAM 48 - WISDOM

 CHALLENGE:

To allow yourself to trust that you'll know what you need to know when you need to know it. To not let the fear of not knowing stop you from creating. To not let "not knowing" hold you back.

 JOURNAL QUESTIONS:

1. Do I trust my own knowing? What needs to be healed, released, aligned and brought to my awareness for me to deepen my self-trust?

2. What practice do I have that keeps me connected to the wisdom of Source? How can I deepen my connection to Source?

AFFIRMATION:

I am a depth of wisdom and knowledge. My studies and experiences have taught me everything I need to know. I push beyond the limits of my earthly knowledge and take great leaps of faith as a function of my deep connection to Source knowing that I'll always know what I need to know when I need to know it.

EFT SETUP:

Even though I'm afraid I'm not ready to, I now choose to courageously dive in and just do it and I deeply and completely love and accept myself.

OCTOBER 8, 2020

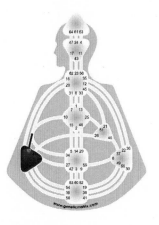

HEXAGRAM 57 - INSTINCT

 **CHALLENGE:**

To learn to trust your own insights and "gut". To learn to tell the difference between an instinctive response versus a fear of the future. To master your connection to your sense of "right" timing.

 JOURNAL QUESTIONS:

1. Do I trust my intuition? What does my intuition feel like to me?

2. Sometimes doing a retrospective analysis of my intuition/instinct makes it more clear how my intuitive signal works. What experiences in the past have I had that I "knew" I should or shouldn't do? How have I experienced my intuition in the past?

3. When I think about moving forward in my life, do I feel afraid? What am I afraid of? What can I do to mitigate the fear?

4. What impulses am I experiencing that are telling me to prepare for what's next in my life? Am I acting on my impulses? Why or why not?

♥ AFFIRMATION:

My Inner Wisdom is deeply connected to the pulse of Divine Timing. I listen to my Inner Wisdom and follow my instinct. I know when and how to prepare the way to prepare for the future. I take guided action and I trust myself and Source.

✋ EFT SETUP:

Even though it's scary to trust my gut, I now choose to honor my awareness, quiet my mind and go with what feels right and I deeply and completely love and accept myself.

OCTOBER 14, 2020

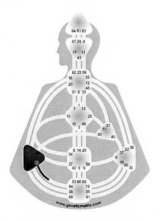

HEXAGRAM 32 - ENDURANCE

 CHALLENGE:

To trust in Divine Timing. To prepare for the next step of manifestation and to align with the unfolding of the process. To be patient.

JOURNAL QUESTIONS:

1. What do I need to do to be prepared to manifest my vision? What actionable steps need to be completed in order for me to be ready when the timing is right?

2. What do I need to do to cultivate patience?

3. Do I have a fear of failing that is causing me to avoid being prepared?

4. Am I over-doing and being overly prepared? Am I pushing too hard? What can I let go of?

 ## AFFIRMATION:

I am a divine translator for Divine Inspiration. I sense and know what needs to be prepared on the earthly plane in order to be ready for right timing. I am aligned with right timing and I prepare and wait patiently knowing that when the time is right I am ready to do the work to help transform pain into power.

 ## EFT SETUP:

Even though I've worked hard to make my dreams come true and nothing has happened yet, I trust in Divine Timing and keep tending to my vision and I deeply and completely love and accept myself.

OCTOBER 16, 2020

NEW MOON

 7:32 PM UTC

 23 DEGREES 52 MINUTES LIBRA

☾ MOON IN GATE 32

New moon energy invites us to explore how we can deepen our alignment with our intentions and asks us to focus on what we want to grow and expand on in our lives.

Gate 32, the Gate of Endurance, is an energy that revolves around two things, timing and readiness. With this energy we are invited to explore whether we are actually prepared to implement our ideas and dreams.

We often get frustrated with timing and think that controlling or managing timing is beyond our reach. You can't control time but you can influence timing. We think we need to wait for the right timing and then get ready but the Quantum Human Design chart shows us that this is actually the wrong order. We are designed to be ready, to set the stage and to have all of our pieces in place before the right timing so that when the timing is right, we are ready to spring into action.

With the New Moon bringing us this energy, we are exploring what we need to prepare to be ready and we're learning to trust in Divine Timing. What do you need to prepare? What dream do you need to be ready to live?

JOURNAL QUESTIONS:

1. What do I need to do to be prepared to manifest my vision? What actionable steps need to be completed in order for me to be ready when the timing is right?

2. What do I need to do to cultivate patience?

3. Do I have a fear of failing that is causing me to avoid being prepared?

4. Am I over-doing and being overly prepared? Am I pushing too hard? What can I let go of?

 AFFIRMATION:

I am a divine translator for Divine Inspiration. I sense and know what needs to be prepared on the earthly plane in order to be ready for right timing. I am aligned with right timing and I prepare and wait patiently knowing that when the time is right I am ready to do the work to help transform pain into power.

OCTOBER 19, 2020

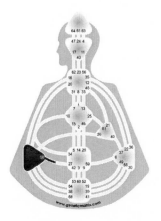

HEXAGRAM 50 - NURTURING

CHALLENGE:

To transcend guilt and unhealthy obligation and do what you need to do to take care of yourself in order to better serve others. To hold to rigid principles to judge others.

JOURNAL QUESTIONS:

1. How do I feel about taking care of myself first? How do I sustain my nurturing energy?

2. What role does guilt play in driving and/or motivating me? What would I choose if I could remove the guilt?

3. Do I have non-negotiable values? What are they? How do I handle people who share different values from me?

 AFFIRMATION:

My presence brings Love into the room. I nurture and love others. I take care of myself first in order to be better able to serve Love. I intuitively know what people need and I facilitate for them a state of self-love and self-empowerment by helping them align more deeply with the power of Love. I let go and I allow others to learn from what I model and teach. I am a deep well of love that sustains the planet.

 EFT SETUP.

Even though it's hard for me to give and receive love, I now choose to be completely open to receiving and sharing deep and unconditional love starting by deeply and completely loving and accepting myself first.

OCTOBER 25, 2020

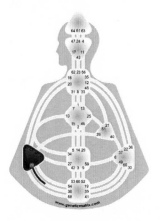

HEXAGRAM 28 - ADVENTURE/CHALLENGE

 **CHALLENGE:**

To not let struggle and challenge leave you feeling defeated and despairing. To learn to face life as an adventure. Do not let challenge and struggle cause you to feel as if you've failed.

 JOURNAL QUESTIONS:

1. *How can I turn my challenge into adventure?*

2. *Where do I need to cultivate a sense of adventure in my life?*

3. What do I need to do to rewrite the story of my "failures"?

4. What meanings, blessings and lessons have I learned from my challenges?

5. What needs to be healed, released, aligned and brought to my awareness for me to trust myself and my choices?

6. What do I need to do to forgive myself for my perceived past failures?

 ## AFFIRMATION:

I am here to push the boundaries of life and what is possible. I thrive in situations that challenge me. I am an explorer on the leading edge of consciousness and my job is to test how far I can go. I embrace challenge. I am an adventurer. I share all that I have learned from my challenges with the world. My stories help give people greater meaning, teach the what is truly worthy of creating and inspire people to transform.

 ## EFT SETUP:

Even though everything feels hard, I now trust that I am mastering what is truly important in my life. I trust the lessons the Universe brings me and I deeply and completely love and accept myself.

OCTOBER 31, 2020

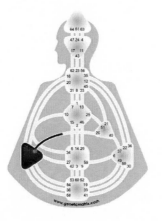

HEXAGRAM 44 - TRUTH

 **CHALLENGE:**

To not get stuck in past patterns. To cultivate the courage to go forward without being stuck in the fear of the past. To learn how to transform pain into power and to have the courage to express your authentic self without compromising or settling.

 JOURNAL QUESTIONS:

1. What patterns from the past are holding me back from moving forward with courage?

2. Do I see how my experiences from the past have helped me learn more about Who I Truly Am? What have I learned about my value and my power?

3. *What needs to be healed, released, aligned and brought to my awareness for me to fully activate my power?*

4. *What needs to be healed, released, aligned and brought to my awareness for me to step boldly into my aligned and authentic path?*

 AFFIRMATION:

I am powerfully intuitive and can sense the patterns that keep others stuck in limiting beliefs and constricted action. Through my insights and awareness I help others break free from past limiting patterns and learn to find the power in their pain, find the blessings in their challenges and help them align more deeply with an authentic awareness of their True Value and Purpose.

 EFT SETUP:

Even though it's hard for me to let go, I deeply and completely love and accept myself.

Even though I am afraid to repeat the past, I now move forward with confidence trusting that I have learned what I needed to learn. I can create whatever future I desire and I deeply and completely love and accept myself.

OCTOBER 31, 2020

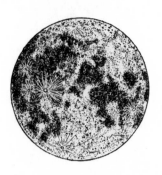

FULL MOON

⏰ 2:51 PM UTC

♉ 8 DEGREES 38 MINUTES TAURUS

☾ MOON IN GATE 24

Full moon energy invites us to explore what we need to release and let go of in order to stay in alignment with our intentions.

Gate 24, the Gate of Blessings, is an energy that helps us find the gift in a situation that has been potentially painful or challenging. When we are hurting we often default to asking the question "why?" (Why did this happen to me? Why did they do that?)

Gate 24 asks us to take a broader perspective, to see our challenges as catalysts for growth and to use pain as a place of learning and deepening of our purpose. This can be a challenging energy as it asks us to rise above the density of the situation and to take a bigger viewpoint, one that inherently invokes an understanding that you are worth more.

It's vital with this energy to check in and make sure you are not rationalizing or settling for less than what you deserve. Can you own your value and hold true to a personal narrative that supports you in claiming and defending your value?

JOURNAL QUESTIONS:

1.   What are the blessings I learned from my greatest painful experiences? Can I see how these experiences served to teach me? What did I learn?

2. What am I grateful for from the past?

3. Where might I be rationalizing staying stuck or settling for less than what I really want or deserve? What do I need to do to break out of this pattern?

 AFFIRMATION:

I embrace the Mystery of Life with the awareness that the infinite generosity of the Universe gives me blessings in every event in my life. I find the blessings from the pain. I grow and expand beyond the limitations of my experiences and stories. I use what I have learned to create a life and circumstances that reflect the miracle that I am.

NOVEMBER 5, 2020

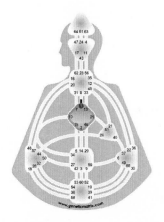

HEXAGRAM 1 - PURPOSE

 CHALLENGE:

To discover a personal, meaningful and world-changing narrative that aligns with a sense of purpose and mission. "I am…" To learn to love yourself enough to honor the idea that your life is the canvas and you are the artist. What you create with your life IS the contribution you give the world.

 JOURNAL QUESTIONS:

1. Am I fully expressing my authentic self?

2. What needs to be healed, released, aligned or brought to my awareness for me to more deeply express my authentic self?

3. *Where am I already expressing who I am?*

4. *Where have I settled or compromised? What needs to change?*

5. *Do I feel connected to my life purpose? What do I need to do to deepen that connection?'*

 AFFIRMATION:

My life is an integral part of the cosmos and the Divine Plan. I honor my life and know that the full expression of who I am is the purpose of my life. The more I am who I am, the more I create a frequency of energy that supports others in doing the same. I commit to exploring all of who I am.

 EFT SETUP:

Even though I am afraid that I am failing my life mission, I now choose to relax and allow my life to unfold before me with ease and grace. I trust that every step I take is perfectly aligned with my soul purpose and I deeply and completely love and accept myself.

NOVEMBER 11, 2020

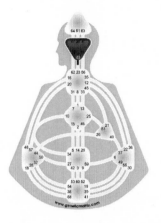

HEXAGRAM 43 - INSIGHT

 CHALLENGE:

To be comfortable and to trust epiphanies and deep inner knowing without doubting what you know. To trust that when the timing is right you will know how to share what you know and serve your role as a transformative messenger who has insights that can change the way people think and what they know.

![inkwell icon] **JOURNAL QUESTIONS:**

1. *Do I trust in Divine Timing?*

2. *Do I trust myself and my own Inner Knowing? What can I do to deepen my connection with my Source of Knowing?*

3. What needs to be healed, released, aligned or brought to my awareness for me to trust my own Inner Knowing?

 ## AFFIRMATION:

I am a vessel of knowledge and wisdom that has the ability to transform the way people think. I share my knowledge with others when they are ready and vibrationally aligned with what I have to share. When the time is right I have the right words and the right insights to help others expand their thinking, re-calibrate their mindset and discover the elegant solutions to the challenges facing Humanity.

 ## EFT SETUP:

Even though it's hard to wait for someone to ask me for my insights, I now choose to wait and know that my thoughts are valuable and precious. I only share them with people who value my insights and I deeply and completely love and accept myself.

NOVEMBER 15, 2020

NEW MOON

⏰ 5:08 AM UTC

♏ 23 DEGREES 17 MINUTES SCORPIO

☾ MOON IN GATE 43

New moon energy invites us to explore how we can deepen our alignment with our intentions and asks us to focus on what we want to grow and expand on in our lives.

Gate 43, the Gate of Insight, sets us up to receive epiphanies and insights today. Since the last full moon we've been exploring the bigger "why" behind our experiences. If you've struggled with the answers you seek, this New Moon energy promises to help you experience a breakthrough in your understanding.

The energy of Gate 43 is tied to "knowingness". This gives us information that we simply "know" without knowing how we know. When this energy is featured in the celestial weather, we are encouraged to explore our relationship with our own self-trust and our knowingness. This energy often comes with profound insights that can change your mindset and your perspectives in a dramatic way that can eventually lead to innovation and transformation.

The mantra for this energy is the trust in your own knowledge and understanding and to allow that you will know what you need to know when you need to know it and once you know it, you don't have to doubt yourself or prove what you to know to others. It is simply YOUR knowing. Own it.

JOURNAL QUESTIONS:

1. *Do I trust in Divine Timing?*

2. *Do I trust myself and my own Inner Knowing? What can I do to deepen my connection with my Source of Knowing?*

3. *What needs to be healed, released, aligned or brought to my awareness for me to trust my own Inner Knowing?*

 AFFIRMATION:

I am a vessel of knowledge and wisdom that has the ability to transform the way people think. I share my knowledge with others when they are ready and vibrationally aligned with what I have to share. When the time is right I have the right words and the right insights to help others expand their thinking, re-calibrate their mindset and discover the elegant solutions to the challenges facing Humanity.

NOVEMBER 16, 2020

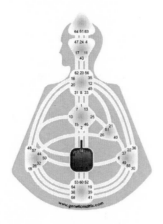

THE 14TH HEXAGRAM - CREATION

 CHALLENGE:

To learn to trust to respond to opportunities that bring resources instead of forcing them or overworking. To learn to value resources and to appreciate how easily they can be created when you are aligned. To be gracious and grateful and not take for granted the resources you have.

 JOURNAL QUESTIONS:

1. Do I trust that I am supported?

2. Am I doing my "right" work? What is the work that feels aligned with my purpose? How is that work showing up in my life right now?

3.   What resources do I have right now that I need to be grateful for?

4.   If I didn't "need" the money, what work would I be doing?

 AFFIRMATION:

I am in the flow of Divine Support. When I trust the generous nature of the Divine and I cultivate a state of faith, I receive all the opportunities and support that I need to evolve my life and transform the world. I know that the right work shows up for me and I am fulfilled in the expression of my life force energy.

EFT SETUP:

Even though I'm afraid that I can't do what I love and make money, I deeply and completely love and accept myself.

NOVEMBER 22, 2020

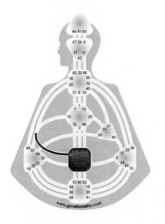

HEXAGRAM 34 - POWER

 CHALLENGE:

To learn to measure out energy in order to stay occupied and busy but to not burn yourself out trying to force the timing or the "rightness" of a project. To wait to know which project or creation to implement based on when you get something to respond to.

JOURNAL QUESTIONS:

1. *Do I trust in Divine Timing? What do I need to do to deepen my trust?*

2. *How do I cultivate greater patience in my life?*

3. *What fears come up for me when I think of waiting? How can I learn to wait with greater faith and ease?*

4. *What do I do to occupy myself while I'm waiting?*

♥ AFFIRMATION:

I am a powerful servant of Divine Timing. When the timing is right, I unify the right people around the right idea and create transformation on the planet. My power is more active when I allow the Universe to set the timing. I wait. I am patient. I trust.

✋ EFT SETUP:

Even though I'm afraid to be powerful, I now choose to fully step into my power and allow the Universe to serve me while I serve it and I deeply and completely love and accept myself.

NOVEMBER 28, 2020

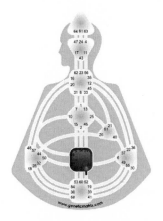

HEXAGRAM 9 - NARROWING

 CHALLENGE:

The energy is about learning where to place your focus. When we work with the energy of this Gate, we have to learn to see the trees AND the forest. This Gate can make us seem "blind" to the big picture and we can lose our focus by getting stuck going down a "rabbit hole"

 JOURNAL QUESTIONS:

1. Where am I putting my energy and attention? Is it creating the growth that I'm seeking?

2. What do I need to focus on?

3. Is my physical environment supporting my staying focused?

4. Do I have a practice that supports me sustaining my focus? What can I do to increase my focus?

 **AFFIRMATION:**

I place my focus and attention on the details that support my creative manifestation. I am clear. I easily see the parts of the whole and I know exactly what to focus on to support my evolution and the evolution of the world.

✋ EFT SETUP:

Even though I've been frustrated with my lack of focus, I now choose to be clear, stay focused and take the actions necessary to create my intentions.

NOVEMBER 30, 2020

PENUMBRAL LUNAR ECLIPSE

🌑 09:32 AM UTC

♊ 8 DEGREES 37 MINUTES GEMINI

☾ MOON IN GATE 16

Full Moon – Gate 16 - November 30 at 09:32 AM UTC 8 degrees 37 minutes Gemini (Penumbral Lunar Eclipse)

Full moon energy invites us to explore what we need to release and let go of in order to stay in alignment with our intentions.

This energy, which also marks a Penumbral Lunar Eclipse, starts a cycle that invites us to not only explore our enthusiasm, but to also look at the role that duality and "either/or" thinking has limited our ability to embrace other possibilities and options. Where have you allowed the limitations of dualistic thinking to keep you from busting out of old patterns and seeing options greater than you realize? It's time to break old patterns and to redefine who we are outside of the confines of dualistic thinking.

Gate 16, the Gate of Zest, gives us an interesting challenge. In its highest expression this is the energy for "doing" that comes with preparation and knowledge. When the timing is right and you've completed enough practice, you are ready to act and share your mastery with the world.

Gate 16 gives us a "gut" impulse that lets us know when the timing is right and when we're ready to act.

In the low expressions of this energy, we fail to act because we think we're not ready or our fear of our inadequacy keeps us stuck and paralyzed or we act too soon, without practice or preparation and we look like fools who have failed to respect our own mastery and the timing of others.

With the Full Moon asking us to release what no longer serves us, Gate 16 energy is asking is to make sure that we're ready, to honor our talent enough to cultivate true mastery through practice and fine tuning our skill but to not be so afraid that we are over-prepared and scared.

 ## JOURNAL QUESTIONS:

1. Do I trust my "gut"?

2. Do I need to slow down and make sure I've done my "homework" before I take action?

3. Have I sidelined my enthusiasm because other people have told me that I "can't" do what I'm dreaming of doing?

 ## AFFIRMATION:

I am a faith-filled contagious force. I take guided actions and I trust my intuition and awareness to let me know when I am prepared and ready to leap into expanding my experience and mastery. My enthusiasm inspires others to trust in themselves and to take their own giant leaps of growth.

DECEMBER 3, 2020

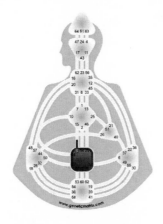

HEXAGRAM 5 - CONSISTENCY

 CHALLENGE:

To learn to craft order, habits and rhythm that support alignment, connection and the flow of Life Force energy and the fulfillment of purpose. To master staying in tune with consistent habits and alignment that support your growth and evolution no matter what is going on around you. Aligning with natural order and staying attuned to the unfolding of the flow of the natural world.

JOURNAL QUESTIONS:

1. What do I need to do to create habits that fuel my energy and keep me vital and feeling connected to myself and Source?

2. What habits do I have that might not be serving my highest expression? How can I change those habits?

3. What kind of environment do I need to cultivate to support my rhythmic nature?

 ## AFFIRMATION:

Consistency gives me power. When I am aligned with my own natural rhythm and the rhythm of life around me I cultivate strength, connection with Source and I am a beacon of stability and order. The order I hold is the touchstone, the returning point of love, that is sustained through cycles of change. The rhythms I maintain set the standard for compassionate action in the world.

EFT SETUP:

Even though I feel nervous/scared/worried about waiting for Divine Timing, I now choose to create habits that support my connection with Source while I wait and I deeply and completely love and accept myself.

DECEMBER 9, 2020

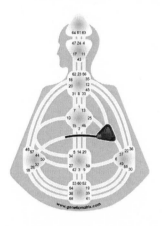

HEXAGRAM 26 - INTEGRITY

 CHALLENGE:

To learn to value your right place and your value enough to act as if you are precious. To heal past traumas and elevate your self-worth. To trust in support enough to do the right thing and to nurture yourself so that you have more to give.

 JOURNAL QUESTIONS:

1. Where might I be experiencing a breech in my moral identity, physical, resource or energy integrity? What do I need to do to bring myself back into integrity?

2. When I act without integrity, can it be traumatic? What trauma do I have that I need to heal? How can I rewrite that story of my trauma as an initiation back into my true value?

3. *What do I need to do right now to nurture myself and to replenish my value?*

 ## AFFIRMATION:

I am a unique, valuable and irreplaceable part of the Cosmic Plan. I am always supported in fulfilling my right place. I take care of my body, my energy, my values and my resources so that I have more to share with the world. I claim and defend my value and fully live in the story of who I am with courage.

 ## EFT SETUP:

Even though I am afraid to share my Truth, I now choose to speak my truth clearly and confidently and I deeply and completely love and accept myself.

DECEMBER 14, 2020

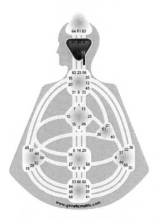

HEXAGRAM 11 - THE CONCEPTUALIST

 ## CHALLENGE:

To sort through and manage all the ideas and inspiration you hold. To trust that the ideas that are yours will show up for you in an actionable way. To value yourself enough to value the ideas you have and to wait for the right people to share those ideas with.

 ## JOURNAL QUESTIONS:

1. What do I do with inspiration when I receive it? Do I know how to serve as a steward for my ideas? Or do I feel pressure to try to force them into form?

2. How much do I value myself? Am I valuing my ideas?

3. *Do I trust the Universe? Do I trust that the ideas that are mine to take action on will manifest in my life according to my Human Design Type and Strategy?*

4. *What can I do to manage the pressure I feel to manifest my ideas? Am I trying to prove my value with my ideas?*

AFFIRMATION:

I am a Divine Vessel of inspiration. Ideas flow to me constantly. I protect and nurture these ideas knowing that my purpose in life is to share ideas and inspiration with others. I use the power of these ideas to stimulate my imagination and the imagination of others. I trust the infinite abundance and alignment of the Universe and I wait for signs to know which ideas are mine to manifest.

EFT SETUP:

Even though I've got so many ideas, I now trust that I will know exactly what action to take and when to take it and I deeply and completely love and accept myself.

DECEMBER 14, 2020

TOTAL SOLAR ECLIPSE

 4:18 PM UTC

 23 DEGREES 07 MINUTES SAGITTARIUS

☾ MOON IN GATE 11

New Moon – Gate 11 on December 14 at 4:18 PM UTC 23 degrees 07 minutes Sagittarius (Total Solar Eclipse in Gate 11, Gate of the Conceptualist)

The total Solar Eclipse in Gate 11, the Gate of the Conceptualist, sets the stage for 2021 and invites you to explore the concept of freedom and what freedom means to you. This will be a great time to travel, plan big and start new projects with focus and presence. 2021 starts off with new big, re-aligned ideas and gives us the hope that 2021 can be a year of building what we truly want for our lives, both individually and collectively.

New moon energy invites us to explore how we can deepen our alignment with our intentions and asks us to focus on what we want to grow and expand on in our lives.

Gate 11, the Gate of the Conceptualist, is an energy that gives us plenty of inspiration and ideas! While this might sound wonderful to some of you, it's an energy that can overwhelm us with possibility causing confusion in our quest to figure out "how" to make all of our ideas a reality.

The real purpose of this energy is to inspire us to think about possibility, to entertain our ideas and use them to increase our emotional excitement and energy and then to wait and see which of our ideas actually bear fruit and show up in our world in alignment with our energy.

Some of the ideas you have this week might not be for you, but for you to share with others. We are all inspired and inspiring this week. Be a steward for the ideas you are receiving.

Nurture the ideas, give them energy and when the timing is right, act on them or give them to their rightful owners.

 JOURNAL QUESTIONS:

1. *What do I do with inspiration when I receive it? Do I know how to serve as a steward for my ideas? Or do I feel pressure to try to force them into form?*

2. *How much do I value myself? Am I valuing my ideas?*

3. *Do I trust the Universe? Do I trust that the ideas that are mine to take action on will manifest in my life according to my Human Design Type and Strategy?*

4. *What can I do to manage the pressure I feel to manifest my ideas? Am I trying to prove my value with my ideas?*

 AFFIRMATION:

I am a Divine Vessel of inspiration. Ideas flow to me constantly. I protect and nurture these ideas knowing that my purpose in life is to share ideas and inspiration with others. I use the power of these ideas to stimulate my imagination and the imagination of others. I trust the infinite abundance and alignment of the Universe and I wait for signs to know which ideas are mine to manifest.

DECEMBER 20, 2020

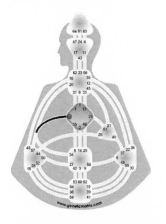

HEXAGRAM 10 - SELF-LOVE

 CHALLENGE:

To learn to love yourself. To learn to take responsibility for your own creations.

JOURNAL QUESTIONS:

1. Do I love myself?

2. What can I do to deepen my self-love?

3. Where can I find evidence of my lovability in my life right now?

4. What do I need to do to take responsibility for situations I hate in my life right now? What needs to change?

5. Where am I holding blame or victimhood in my life? How could I turn that energy around?

🖤 AFFIRMATION:

I am an individuated aspect of the Divine. I am born of Love. My nature is to Love and be Loved. I am in the full flow of giving and receiving Love. I know that the quality of Love that I have for myself, sets the direction for what I attract into my life. I am constantly increasing the quality of love I experience and sharing with the world.

✋ EFT SETUP:

Even though it I struggle with loving myself, I now choose to be open to discovering how to love myself anyway and I deeply and completely love and accept myself.

DECEMBER 25, 2020

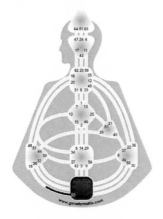

GATE 58 - THE JOY OF MASTERY

 CHALLENGE:

To follow the drive to create the fulfillment of your potential. To learn to craft a talent and make it masterful through joyful learning and repetition. To learn to embrace joy as a vital force of creative power without guilt or denial.

 JOURNAL QUESTIONS:

1. *What brings me the greatest joy? How can I deepen my practice of joy?*

2. *How can I create more joy in my life?*

3.   *What keeps me from fulfilling my potential and my talent? What am I afraid of?*

 ## AFFIRMATION:

I am a masterful curator of my own talent. I use my joy to drive me to master the fun expression of all that I am. I practice as my path to mastery. I know that from repetition and consistency comes a more masterful expression of my talent. I embrace learning and growing, and I commit to the full expression of my joy.

 ## EFT SETUP:

Even though it's hard to let go of the past, I now choose to release it and embrace all the joy that is available to me right now and I deeply and completely love and accept myself.

DECEMBER 30, 2020

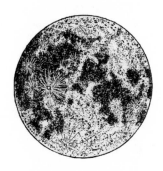

FULL MOON

 3:30 AM UTC

 8 DEGREES 53 MINUTES CANCER

☾ MOON IN GATE 39

Full moon energy invites us to explore what we need to release and let go of in order to stay in alignment with our intentions.

Gate 39, the Gate of Re-Calibration, can be a tricky energy. It has the power to provoke us, to force us to face the things in our life that are creating a consciousness of lack versus abundance. We can get triggered with this energy, causing us to be defensive and to justify the evidence for our lack of faith.

Or we can use the power of this provocation to explore where we may be limiting what we are allowing into our lives because our faith "muscle" needs some strengthening.

With the Full Moon bringing us an opportunity for release, we explore this week those places where our faith is supporting us in creating more than what our human mind is seeing as possible or those spaces that need re-alignment with abundance and a strengthening of our faith.

JOURNAL QUESTIONS:

1. Do I trust Source? What do I need to do to deepen my trust in Source?

2. Do I feel like I am "enough"? Do I feel like I have "enough"?

3. Take stock of everything I have and everything I've been given. Do I have enough? Have I ever really not been supported?

4. What do I have that I'm grateful for?

5. Have I abdicated my own power to create? What needs to be healed, released, aligned or brought to my awareness to reactive my power to create my own abundance?

 AFFIRMATION:

I am deeply calibrated with my faith. I trust that I am fully supported. I use experiences that create desire and wanting in me as opportunities to deepen my faith that I will receive and create all that I need to fulfill my mind, body and spirit. I am in the perfect flow of abundance and I am deeply aligned with Source.

DECEMBER 31, 2020

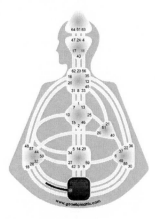

HEXAGRAM 38 - VISIONARY

 **CHALLENGE:**

To experience challenge as a way of knowing what's worth fighting for. To turn the story of struggle into a discovery of meaning and to let the power of what you discover serve as a foundation for a strong vision of transformation that brings dreams into manifested form.

 JOURNAL QUESTIONS:

1. Do I know what's worth committing to and fighting for in my life?

2. Do I have a dream that I am sharing with the world?

3. Do I know how to use my struggles and challenges as the catalyst for creating deeper meaning in the world? In my life?

 AFFIRMATION:

My challenges, struggles and adventures have taught me about what is truly valuable in life. I use my understandings to hold a vision of what else is possible for the world. I am aligned with the values that reflect the preciousness of life and I sustain a vision for a world that is aligned with Heart. My steadfast commitment to my vision inspires others to join me in creating a world of equitable, sustainable peace.

 **EFT SETUP:**

"Even though things seem hard and challenging, I now choose to use my challenges to help me get clear about what I really want, and I deeply and completely love and accept myself."

JANUARY 5, 2021

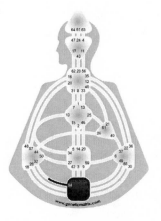

HEXAGRAM 54 - DIVINE INSPIRATION

 CHALLENGE:

To learn to be a conduit for Divine Inspiration. To be patient and to wait for alignment and right timing before taking action. To be at peace with stewardship for ideas and to learn to trust the divine trajectory of an inspiration.

 JOURNAL QUESTIONS:

1. *What do I do to get inspired? How do I interface with my creative muse?*

2. *Is there anything I need to do or prepare in order to be ready for the next step in the manifestation of my dream or inspiration?*

AFFIRMATION:

I am a Divine Conduit for inspiration. Through me new ideas about creating sustainability and peace on the planet are born. I tend to my inspirations, give them love and energy and prepare the way for their manifestations in the material world.

 ## EFT SETUP:

"Even though I'm afraid my dreams won't come true, I now choose to dream wildly and trust that my dreams will come true. All I have to do is focus my mind, trust and know that all will unfold perfectly and I deeply and completely love and accept myself."

JANUARY 11, 2021

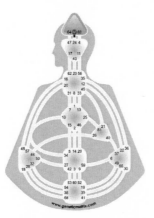

HEXAGRAM 61 - WONDER

CHALLENGE:

To not get lost in trying to answer or figure out why? To maintain a state of wonder. To not let the pressure of trying to "know" keep you from being present.

JOURNAL QUESTIONS:

1. *What do I do to maintain my sense of wonder? How can I deepen my awe of the magnificence of the Universe?*

2. *What old thoughts, patterns and beliefs do I need to release in order to align with my knowingness and to trust my "delusional confidence" as a powerful creative state.*

3. What greater perspectives on the events of my life can I see? What are the greatest lessons I've learned from my pain? How do I use these lessons to expand my self-expression?

 AFFIRMATION:

I have a direct connection to a cosmic perspective that gives me an expanded view of the meaning of the events in my life and the lives of others. I see the wonder and innocence of life and stay present in a constant state of awe. I am innocent and pure in my understanding of the world and my innocence is the source of my creative alignment.

✋ **EFT SETUP:**

Even though I don't know all the answers, I now choose to surrender and trust that I am being loved, supported and nurtured by the Infinite Loving Source that is the Universe.

JANUARY 13, 2021

NEW MOON

🔔 05:02 AM UTC

♑ 23 DEGREES 13 MINUTES CAPRICORN

☾ MOON IN GATE 61

New moon energy invites us to explore how we can deepen our alignment with our intentions and asks us to focus on what we want to grow and expand on in our lives.

Gate 61, the Gate of Wonder, represents the energy in the Quantum Human Design chart where we connect with Source at the purest level. The energy of wonder and awe literally expands our minds and what we know is possible for our lives and the world.

This energy can flow into our awareness giving us expanded understandings, bigger perspectives and ideas that have the potential to transcend the patterns and possibilities we are currently living out. This is deep, esoteric understandings and epiphanies that can transform thinking on a dime. Once you know what this energy brings you, you can't go back to not knowing.

This New Moon sets us up for the new year, restoring to us our innocence and the idea that anything we can dream of is possible. Take some time during this New Moon to simply dream and cultivate a state of wonder about your life. This is an initiation into transformative thinking and powerful mindset shifting that will set the tone for what you believe is possible for your life.

JOURNAL QUESTIONS:

1. *What do I do to maintain my sense of wonder? How can I deepen my awe of the magnificence of the Universe?*

2. *What old thoughts, patterns and beliefs do I need to release in order to align with my knowingness and to trust my "delusional confidence" as a powerful creative state.*

3. *What greater perspectives on the events of my life can I see? What are the greatest lessons I've learned from my pain? How do I use these lessons to expand my self-expression?*

 AFFIRMATION:

I have a direct connection to a cosmic perspective that gives me an expanded view of the meaning of the events in my life and the lives of others. I see the wonder and innocence of life and stay present in a constant state of awe. I am innocent and pure in my understanding of the world and my innocence is the source of my creative alignment.

JANUARY 16, 2021

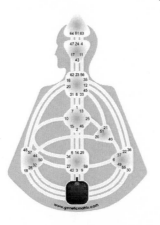

HEXAGRAM 60 - RESOURCEFULNESS

 ## CHALLENGE:

To not let the fear of loss overwhelm your resourcefulness. To learn to find what is working and focus on it instead of looking at the loss and disruption.

 ## JOURNAL QUESTIONS:

1. *What change am I resisting? What am I afraid of?*

2. *What are the things in my life that are working that I need to focus on?*

3. *Is my fear of loss holding me back?*

 AFFIRMATION:

I am grateful for all the transformation and change in my life. I know that disruption is the catalyst for my growth. I am able to find the blessings of the past and incorporate them in my innovative vision for the future. I am optimistic about the future and I transform the world by growing what works.

 EFT SETUP.

Even though it's hard to let go of things that didn't work, I now release all the clutter from the past and I deeply and completely love, accept and trust myself.

SUMMARY

Your Human Design is your key to understanding your energy, your Life Purpose, your Life Path, and your Soul's Journey in this life time. You are a once-in-a-lifetime cosmic event and the fulfillment of your potential and purpose is the greatest gift you can give the world.

I hope this year has been revolutionary for you and that you re-connected with the True story of Who You Are and the power and possibility of your very special life.

If you need additional support and resources to help you on your life path and soul's journey, please visit www.quantumalignmentsystem.com, where you can find Specialists and Practitioners who will help you understand the story of your Human Design chart, coach you, and help you get to the root of any pain, blocks, or limiting beliefs that may be keeping you from enjoying your Life Story. There are all kinds of free goodies, videos, e-books, and resources to help you on your way!

Thank you again for being YOU! We are who we are because you are who you are!

From my Heart to Yours,

Karen

ABOUT THE AUTHOR

Karen Parker is a #1 best-selling author, Human Design specialist, trainer, professional speaker, and futurist. She has been a high-performance life and business coach for more than 25 years and has coached over 8,000 people. She is deeply dedicated to sharing and co-creating a sustainable, abundant global community.

Karen is the author of:

» *Understanding Human Design the New Science of Astrology: Discover Who You Really Are,*
» *Human Design Activation Guide: Introduction to Your Quantum Blueprint,*
» *Inside the Body of God: 13 Strategies for Thriving in the Quantum World*
» *Abundance by Design: Discover Your Unique Code for Health, Wealth and Happiness With Human Design*
» *The Prosperity Revolution,*
» *EFT for Parents,*
» *Waging Peace in the Face of Rage*

and weekly articles about abundance and spirituality. She is the host of the internationally acclaimed podcast, Quantum Conversations. Karen's work has been featured on Fox News, Bloomberg Businessweek, CBS, ABC, and various radio shows and telesummits.

Karen's website:
www.quantumalignmentsystem.com

Karen is available for private consultations, keynote talks, and to conduct in-house seminars and workshops.

You can reach her at Karen@quantumalignmentsystem.com.

Made in United States
North Haven, CT
13 March 2024

49909766R00114